Contents

Chemistry

Contents

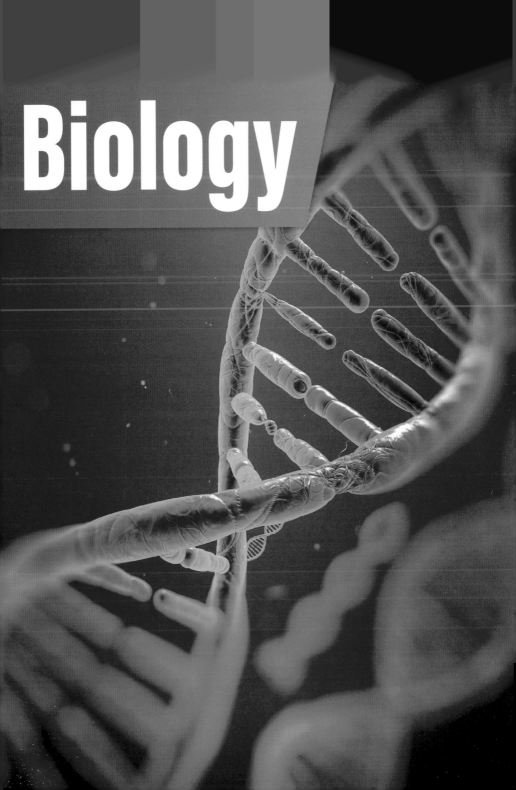

Biology

Microscopy

Microscopes create magnified images of objects, such as cells, so they can be seen in more detail.

Light Microscope

The light microscope uses light waves and lenses to magnify objects.

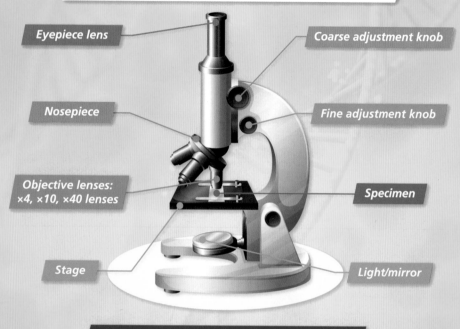

- Eyepiece lens
- Coarse adjustment knob
- Nosepiece
- Fine adjustment knob
- Objective lenses: ×4, ×10, ×40 lenses
- Specimen
- Stage
- Light/mirror

Onion cell biological drawing (Magnification × 100)

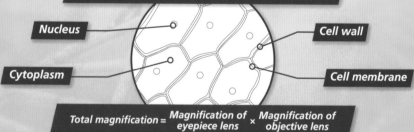

- Nucleus
- Cell wall
- Cytoplasm
- Cell membrane

$$\text{Total magnification} = \text{Magnification of eyepiece lens} \times \text{Magnification of objective lens}$$

Magnification is how much larger an image is compared to the real object.

$$\text{Actual Size} = \frac{\text{Image size}}{\text{Magnification}}$$

Microscopic objects are measured using these units:		
Millimetres	mm	$1 \times 10^{-3}\,m$
Micrometres	µm	$1 \times 10^{-6}\,m$
Nanometres	nm	$1 \times 10^{-9}\,m$
Picometres	pm	$1 \times 10^{-12}\,m$

 daydream EDUCATION

Example

The image of a cell viewed at ×40 magnification has a diameter of 1 mm. What is the cell's real diameter?

1 Substitute the numbers into the formula:

$$\text{Actual size} = \frac{1}{40}$$

2 Solve:

Actual size = 0.025 mm or 25 μm

Electron Microscope

The electron microscope uses a beam of electrons to magnify objects.

The light microscope was invented in the 16th century, but a major advance in microscopy came in the 1930s with the invention of the electron microscope.

An electron microscope has a much higher magnification and resolution than a light microscope so smaller things can be seen in more detail.

Resolution is the ability to distinguish between two separate points.

A typical light microscope has a **resolving power** of 200 nm. This means it can distinguish between points 200 nm apart. The resolving power of an electron microscope is up to 0.2 nm.

The development of electron microscopes has enabled scientists to see structures more clearly and in more detail, which has increased our understanding of microscopic objects such as cells.

Light Microscope

Electron Microscope

Bacteria viewed on a light microscope and an electron microscope

Cell Structure

Prokaryotic

Prokaryotic cells, such as bacteria, are single celled organisms. They are a lot smaller than eukaryotic cells and their genetic material is not enclosed in a nucleus.

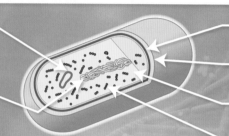

Plasmid
Small loops of DNA that are not part of the chromosomal DNA

Chromosomal DNA
A long loop of genetic material that is not enclosed in a nucleus

Cell Membrane

Cell Wall

Cytoplasm

Ribosomes

Eukaryotic

Eukaryotic cells are found in animals and plants, as well as in fungi and protists. They have a cell membrane, cytoplasm and genetic material that is enclosed in a nucleus.

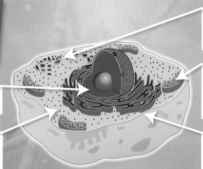

Animal Cells
Most animal cells have the following subcellular structure:

Nucleus
Contains genetic material

Cytoplasm
Made up of a liquid gel that holds all cellular organelles; the place where chemical reactions occur

Ribosomes
The place where proteins are produced

Mitochondria
The place where aerobic respiration, which releases energy, occurs

Cell Membrane
A thin, selectively permeable membrane that controls which substances can enter and exit the cell

Plant Cells
Most plant cells have the same subcellular structure as animal cells, plus:

Cell Wall
Made of cellulose, which strengthens and protects the cell

Large Central Vacuole
Filled with cell sap; stores materials and waste; and keeps the cell turgid (rigid)

Chloroplasts
Contains chlorophyll; the place where photosynthesis occurs

Cell Specialisation & Differentiation

Cell Specialisation
Cells may be specialised to carry out a specific function.

Animal Cells

Sperm Cells

The **acrosome** contains enzymes to help break down the egg membrane.

The **haploid nucleus** contains half the number of chromosomes of a normal cell.

Mitochondria provide energy to power the tail.

The **long tail** and streamlined shape enable the sperm to swim to the egg.

Nerve Cells

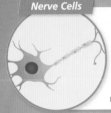

Nerve cells (neurons) are highly specialised for transmitting impulses around the body. They are long and have branched connections to join to other neurons and form networks.

Muscle Cells

Muscle cells contain lots of mitochondria to provide energy. These cells can contract and relax, and they can also store glucose as glycogen.

Plant Cells

Xylem Cells

Xylem vessels transport water and strengthen plant structures. They are made of dead cells that have lost their end walls and cytoplasm to become hollow tubes for transporting water. Their walls are thickened with lignin to provide strength.

Root Hair Cells

Root hair cells are found in the roots of plants and are specialised for absorbing water and mineral ions. They have hair-like projections that provide a large surface area for water absorption.

Phloem Cells

Phloem vessels transport sugars (sucrose) in plants. Phloem cells have perforated end walls and a very thin layer of cytoplasm to aid transport. Each cell has an attached companion cell, which supplies materials the cytoplasm normally makes.

Cell Differentiation

When new cells are formed in organisms, they are simple in form. However, over time, they differentiate (become specialised) to form different types of cells.

Most types of animal cell differentiate early in life – many in the embryo – whereas many types of plant cell retain the ability to differentiate throughout their life.

In mature animals, new cells are still formed by cell division to replace old cells and to repair tissues. As the cell differentiates into a specialised cell, it adopts different subcellular structures. For example, cells in the bone marrow differentiate into new red blood cells. The cells lose their nucleus, change shape and become filled with the red, oxygen-carrying pigment, haemoglobin.

daydream EDUCATION

Cell Division & the Cell Cycle

Cells divide in a series of stages called the cell cycle. In multicellular organisms, cell division is used for growth and repairing damaged tissues. It is also used by some organisms for asexual reproduction.

Chromosomes

The nucleus of a cell contains structures called chromosomes, which are made of DNA molecules. Along each chromosome are sections called genes.

Each gene controls the manufacture of a particular protein, and these proteins determine the characteristics of the organism. In body cells, the chromosomes exist in pairs. For instance, in humans, there are 23 pairs.

Mitosis and the Cell Cycle

During the cell cycle, a cell's DNA and subcellular structures are replicated before the cell divides by a process called mitosis to produce two identical daughter cells.

2 DNA Copied

The DNA replicates to form two copies of each chromosome, and the copies form an X shape.

Interphase

DNA Copied

Cell Matures

Cell Prepares for Division

Cytokinesis

Mitosis

Cellular Division

Daughter Cells

1 Cell Matures

Before dividing, a cell needs to grow and increase the number of subcellular structures such as ribosomes and mitochondria.

3 Cell Prepares for Division

The cell grows quickly and continues with protein synthesis in preparation for mitosis. Any damaged DNA is also repaired.

4 Mitosis

During mitosis, cells divide into identical cells. Each set of chromosomes is pulled to either end of the cell, and the nucleus divides.

Prophase	Metaphase	Anaphase	Telophase	Cytokinesis
The nucleus breaks down, and spindle fibres form.	The chromosomes line up at the centre of the cell and attach to the spindle fibres.	The replicated chromosomes separate and move to opposite ends of the cell.	Membranes develop around each set of chromosomes to form the nuclei of the two new cells.	The cytoplasm and membrane of the parent cell divide, forming two identical daughter cells.

In plant cells, a new cell wall will form to divide the cells.

daydream
EDUCATION

Stem Cells

A stem cell is an undifferentiated cell (i.e. one that has not yet specialised) that can give rise to more cells of the same type or can develop into certain other cells by differentiation.

Stem Cells in Embryos

At an early stage of development, an embryo is a ball of cells. Each cell will divide and later give rise to all the different types of cells in the body.

These cells can be cloned and made to develop into most cell types in a laboratory.

Stem Cells in Adult Animals

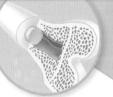

Stem cells are present in adult animals. For example, bone marrow inside the cavities of bones can naturally form blood cells.

These cells can also be manipulated in a laboratory to differentiate into some other cell types.

Stem Cells in Plants

Plants have stem cells that can develop into all types of plant cell throughout the life of the plant.

They are mainly found in specific growing points, called meristems, at the tips of roots and shoots.

Medical Uses of Stem Cells

Stem cells can potentially be used to replace damaged cells and repair tissues. Therefore, they can be used to help with conditions such as type 1 diabetes and paralysis. However, if a patient is treated with stem cells from another individual, the immune system may attack the new cells and reject them.

The use of stem cells has some potential risks. For example, viruses live inside cells, and it is possible that a viral infection could be transferred in the stem cells.

Some people also have ethical or religious objections because embryos are destroyed when obtaining stem cells. Although adult stem cells can be used for some treatments, they cannot develop into as many types of cell as embryonic stem cells can.

In therapeutic cloning, a nucleus is taken from a cell of the patient and transplanted into an unfertilised egg cell. The egg cell can then produce stem cells that are genetically identical to those of the patient and will not be rejected.

Uses of Plant Stem Cells

Meristem cells in plants are mainly used to produce clones – and specifically, large numbers of genetically identical plants.

Rare species can be cloned to protect from extinction, and when new varieties of crop plants are produced with beneficial features (e.g. disease resistance), they can be cloned to produce large numbers of plants quickly.

Diffusion

Diffusion is the spreading out of gas or solute particles from an area of higher concentration to an area of lower concentration.

Diffusion takes place across cell membranes to enable the movement of substances into and out of cells.

Particles move both ways across a membrane. However, if there are more particles on one side, the net (overall) movement will be from an area of higher concentration to an area of lower concentration until the concentrations on both sides are equal.

Before **After**

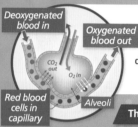

Deoxygenated blood in
Oxygenated blood out
CO_2 out
O_2 in
Red blood cells in capillary
Alveoli

In the lungs, oxygen from the air diffuses into the blood in the capillaries. Carbon dioxide from the blood diffuses into the air in the alveoli.

Urea is a waste product produced in liver cells. It diffuses from cells into the blood, and then travels to the kidneys where it is excreted.

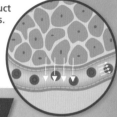

The following factors affect the rate of diffusion:

Concentration Gradient

The bigger the difference between the concentrations, the faster the rate of diffusion.

Membrane Surface Area

The larger the surface area of the membrane, the faster the rate of diffusion, because more particles can pass through at the same time.

Temperature

At a higher temperature, particles have more energy and therefore move quicker.

Surface Area to Volume Ratio

As a cell gets larger, its **surface area** to **volume ratio** gets smaller. You can calculate and compare **surface area** to **volume ratio** as follows.

A   B

Shape	Side Length	Area of Each Face	Total Surface Area	Volume	Surface Area to Volume Ratio
A	2 cm	$2 \times 2 = 4$ cm²	$4 \times 6 = 24$ cm²	$2 \times 2 \times 2 = 8$ cm³	24:8 = 3:1
B	4 cm	$4 \times 4 = 16$ cm²	$16 \times 6 = 96$ cm²	$4 \times 4 \times 4 = 64$ cm³	96:64 = 3:2

The table above shows that shape A has a surface area to volume ratio of 3:1, and that shape B has a surface area to volume ratio of 3:2. Therefore, the surface area to volume ratio of shape A (the smaller shape) is larger than surface area to volume ratio of shape B.

daydream
EDUCATION

Single-Celled Organisms and Multicellular Organisms

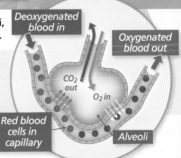

Bronchus
Ciliated cell
Capillary
Alveoli
Goblet cell

A single-celled organism has a large surface area to volume ratio. As a result, its surface area is large enough to allow sufficient diffusion of substances through its membranes to meet its needs.

However, larger multicellular organisms have smaller surface area to volume ratios and therefore need specialised gas exchange surfaces and transport systems to assist with the exchange of substances.

Look at how the lungs are adapted to increase gas exchange.

1 The lungs contain millions of tiny air sacs called alveoli, which provide a **large surface area** for gas exchange.

2 The walls of the alveoli are only one cell thick, creating a **short diffusion path**. They are also moist, so oxygen and carbon dioxide can be dissolved and diffused more quickly.

3 The alveoli are covered in a mesh of capillaries, which provide a **constant supply of blood** so that large volumes of gases can be exchanged.

Deoxygenated blood in
Oxygenated blood out
CO_2 out
O_2 in
Red blood cells in capillary
Alveoli

Oxygen diffuses from the air into the blood, and carbon dioxide diffuses from the blood into the air. Both do so along **steep concentration gradients**, which are maintained by **ventilation** and the flow of blood through capillaries in the lungs.

Other Examples

Mammals
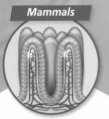

The small intestines are lined with tiny projections called villi, which aid the absorption of nutrients. They have a large surface area, thin walls (one cell thick) and a good blood supply.

Plants

Plant leaves have a large surface area to maximise the absorption of carbon dioxide. They are also thin so that carbon dioxide does not have far to diffuse into the leaf.

Fish

Fish have specially adapted gills that are highly folded to provide a large surface area. The flow of water and blood through the gills also ensures steep concentration gradients.

Active Transport & Osmosis

Active Transport

Low concentration

Cell membrane   Transport protein

Energy

High concentration

Active transport occurs when molecules need to be moved against a concentration gradient or they are too big to diffuse through the membrane. This process requires energy from respiration.

Transport proteins capture the molecules and transfer them across the cell membrane.

Active transport is used by plants to take up mineral ions from the soil because the concentration of mineral ions is much lower in the soil than in the root cells.

Active transport is also used to absorb sugar molecules from the gut into the blood. This allows absorption to continue even if the concentration of sugar in the gut is lower than in the blood.

Osmosis

Osmosis is the diffusion of water across a partially permeable membrane from a dilute solution to a concentrated solution.

A partially permeable membrane allows molecules to pass through it in both directions. However, large molecules, such as salt, are too big to fit through.

If the concentration of water is higher on one side of the membrane, it will diffuse through the membrane to the side where the concentration is lower. The net movement will stop when the concentration of water is the same on both sides.

Osmosis is used by plants to absorb water from the soil through their root hair cells.

● Salt ● Water

High water conc.   **Low water conc.**

Osmosis can cause tissue to gain or lose mass. To calculate the change in mass, the following formula can be used:

$$\text{Percentage change in mass} = \frac{\text{Change in mass}}{\text{Initial mass}} \times 100$$

daydream
EDUCATION

Osmosis can be investigated by placing cylinders of potato into different concentrations of salt or sugar solution. In this activity, we will use sugar.

1 Cut the potatoes into evenly sized cylinders so that they have the same surface area.

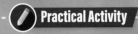

2 Pour different concentrations of sugar solution (0.2 molL^{-1}, 0.4 molL^{-1}, 0.6 molL^{-1}, 0.8 molL^{-1}) into beakers.

3 Measure the mass of each cylinder.
Then place one in each beaker and leave them for 24 hours.

4 Take the cylinders out of the solution, dry them and then measure their masses again.

5 Calculate the percentage change in mass of each potato using the formula:

$$\text{% Change in mass} = \frac{\text{Change in mass}}{\text{Original mass}} \times 100$$

6 Plot a graph to show the results, with sugar concentration on the x-axis and percentage change in mass on the y-axis.

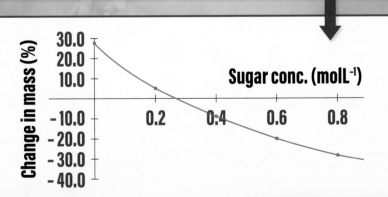

If the cylinder has decreased in mass, it has lost water. If the cylinder has increased in mass, it has gained water. If there is no change in mass, the concentrations of the solution and the potato sap are the same, and water moves in and out at equal rates.

Cell Organisation & Organ Systems

Cell Organisation

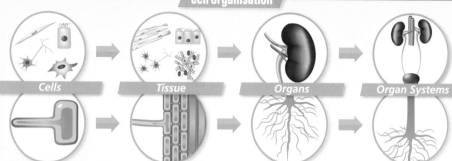

Cells

Cells are the basic building blocks of all living organisms.

Tissue

A tissue is a group of cells with a similar structure and function.

Organs

Organs are collections of different tissues that perform specific functions.

Organ Systems

Organs work together in systems to form organisms.

Some Human Organs

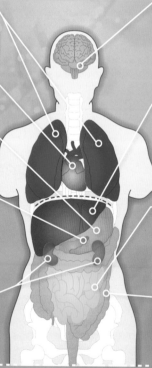

Lungs

The lungs help us breathe. They take in oxygen from the air and expel carbon dioxide into the air.

Heart

The heart is a pump. It pumps blood around the body.

Stomach

The stomach helps to digest food before it passes into the intestines.

Pancreas

The pancreas helps with the digestion of food by secreting digestive enzymes. It also secretes the hormones insulin and glucagon to help control blood sugar levels.

Kidneys

The kidneys filter waste from the blood and expel excess water and salts from the body in the form of urine.

Brain

The brain is the control centre for movement, sleep, hunger, thirst and virtually every other vital activity necessary for survival.

Liver

The liver is like a chemical factory that adjusts food levels in the blood. It removes toxins from the blood and generates body heat.

Small Intestine

The small intestine is the longest section of the digestive system and is where most digestion occurs.

Large Intestine

Indigestible food goes to the large intestine. Water is absorbed, and the remaining food becomes faeces.

daydream
EDUCATION

The 11 Human Organ Systems

The human body is made up of 11 major organ systems.

Digestive System

Digests (breaks down) and absorbs food so that it can be used by the body

Muscular System

Controls movement and helps to maintain posture

Circulatory System

Circulates blood and transports oxygen, carbon dioxide and nutrients around the body

Respiratory System

Facilitates gaseous exchange by moving air into the lungs and removing carbon dioxide

Skeletal System

Performs vital functions, including support, movement, protection, blood cell production, calcium storage and endocrine regulation

Integumentary System

Protects the body from damage and helps with the retention of body fluids, removal of waste and regulation of body temperature

Lymphatic & Immune System

Protects against infection, returns excess interstitial fluid to the circulatory system and transports dietary fats

Endocrine System

Secretes hormones into the bloodstream to regulate bodily functions such as metabolism, growth and tissue function

Urinary System

Removes waste from the body as urine; regulates water and salt levels in the blood

Nervous System

Coordinates actions and transmits signals to and from different parts of the body

Reproductive System

Female
Produces egg cells and supports the development of offspring

Male
Produces and transports sperm for reproduction

The Human Digestive System

In the human digestive system, several organs work together to digest and absorb food.

Food is mostly made up of complex organic compounds (e.g. carbohydrates, proteins, fats) that must be broken down into simple inorganic compounds so that they can be absorbed into the blood system. This breakdown is catalysed by enzymes.

Structure and Function in the Human Digestive System

Mouth
Saliva in the mouth lubricates food and contains the enzyme, amylase, which breaks down starch (a carbohydrate) into maltose sugar.

Liver
The liver makes bile, which is stored in the gall bladder and helps break down fats.

Gall Bladder
The gall bladder stores bile.

Pancreas
The pancreas secretes enzymes that break down various food chemicals in the small intestine.

Rectum
The rectum stores solid waste and then passes it out via the anus.

Oesophagus
The oesophagus moves food to the stomach using peristalsis (wave-like muscle contractions).

Stomach
The stomach releases the enzyme protease, which breaks down proteins into amino acids. Hydrochloric acid in the stomach also kills harmful pathogens.

Small Intestine
Enzymes complete digestion, and nutrients are then absorbed into the blood, so they can be transported around the body.

Large Intestine
The large intestine reabsorbs water.

Food Type	Enzymes Used	End Product
Complex carbohydrates	Carbohydrases	Simple sugars
Proteins	Proteases	Amino acids
Lipids (fats)	Lipases	Glycerol and fatty acids

daydream EDUCATION

Bile

Bile is an alkaline digestive fluid produced in the liver and stored in the gall bladder. It is released into the small intestine via the bile duct. It contains no enzymes but serves two vital functions:

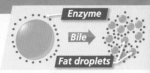

1 It neutralises the acid that is added to food in the stomach. If the pH level in the small intestine is too low, the enzymes won't work properly.

2 It emulsifies fats. Large fat droplets are broken up into many smaller ones, so that there is a greater surface area over which enzymes can act.

The products of digestion are used in the body to build new carbohydrates, proteins and fats. Some glucose is used directly to provide energy by respiration.

Practical Activity

There are a wide variety of tests that are used to identify carbohydrates, lipids and proteins.

Testing for Starch

Add iodine solution to the sample. If starch is present, the mixture of the sample and iodine solution will change colour from orange-brown to blue-black.

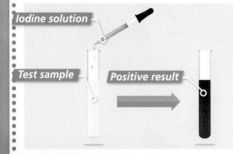

Iodine solution

Test sample — Positive result

Testing for Simple Sugars

Add Benedict's solution to the sample, and place it in a hot water bath (75–80°C). If sugar is present, a colour change occurs from blue to green, yellow, orange and then red. A precipitate will form, making the sample cloudy.

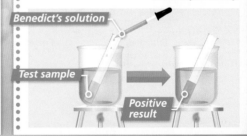

Benedict's solution

Test sample

Positive result

Testing for Protein

Biuret solution is added to the sample, sometimes in two parts: biuret A (sodium hydroxide) and biuret B (copper sulfate). If protein is present, the solution will change colour from blue to purple.

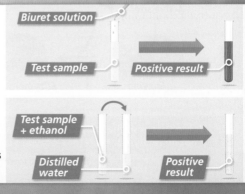

Biuret solution

Test sample — Positive result

Testing for Lipids

Lipids are detected using the emulsion test. Mix the test sample with 2 cm³ of ethanol and add an equal volume of distilled water. If lipids are present a milky-white emulsion will form.

Test sample + ethanol

Distilled water

Positive result

Enzymes

Enzymes are proteins that act as biological catalysts. They are produced by living organisms to speed up chemical reactions in the body.

Key Terminology

Catalyst: Catalysts increase the rate of chemical reactions but are not used up during the reaction. Different reactions need different catalysts.

Enzyme Action

Enzymes are formed from chains of amino acids that are folded in a particular way to create a small pocket called the active site.

The molecule upon which an enzyme acts, or the substrate, also has a specific shape, which fits together with the shape of the active site. This is known as the lock-and-key mechanism. Enzymes can both split apart and join substrates to form products.

The Lock-and-Key Mechanism

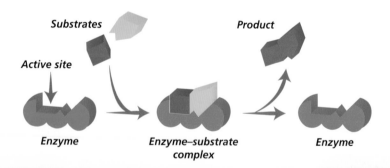

Substrate — Active site — Enzyme — Enzyme–substrate complex — Enzyme — Products

Substrates — Active site — Enzyme — Enzyme–substrate complex — Enzyme — Product

If the shapes of the enzyme and substrate do not match, then the reaction will not be catalysed. Therefore, enzymes can only work with specific substrates.
It is now known that the enzyme needs to change its shape slightly to perfectly match the shape of the substrate. This is called the induced-fit model.

daydream
EDUCATION

Enzyme Activity

Enzymes are affected by their surrounding conditions. Temperature, pH, and substrate and enzyme concentration are all factors that can affect the rate of enzyme-controlled reactions.

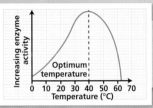

As temperature increases, so does the rate of reaction. However, at high temperatures, some of the bonds that hold the enzyme together break, changing the shape of the active site so the enzyme becomes denatured.

Different enzymes work best at different pHs. If the pH changes too far from the optimum, the bonds holding the enzyme together weaken, changing the shape of the active site so the enzyme becomes denatured.

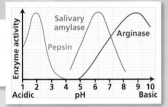

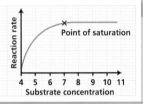

As substrate concentration increases, so does the rate of reaction as there are more substrate molecules to collide with enzyme molecules. However, after a certain concentration, any increase has no effect on the rate of reaction because the enzymes are working at their maximum rate.

Uses of Enzymes

1 Digestion

Enzymes break down large molecules into smaller molecules so they can be used for growth, respiration and other life processes.

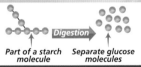

Part of a starch molecule → Separate glucose molecules

Complex carbohydrates (starches) are broken down into glucose by carbohydrases such as amylase.

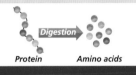

Protein → Amino acids

Proteins are broken down into amino acids by proteases.

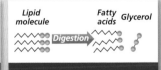

Lipid molecule → Fatty acids Glycerol

Lipids are converted into glycerol and fatty acids by lipases.

2 Metabolism

Metabolism refers to all the chemical reactions in an organism. These reactions use energy and are catalysed by enzymes. Examples include:

Conversion of glucose to starch, glycogen and cellulose	Formation of lipids from a molecule of glycerol and three molecules of fatty acids	Using glucose and nitrate ions to form amino acids, which form proteins	Breakdown of excess proteins to form the waste product urea	Respiration

The Heart & Blood Vessels

The Heart

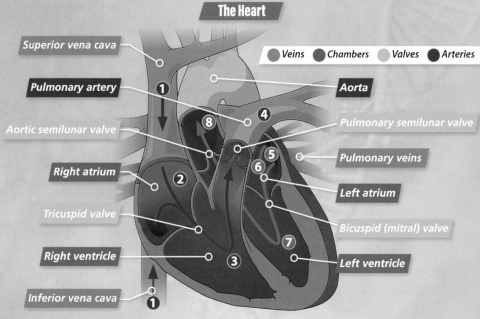

Veins **Chambers** **Valves** **Arteries**

Superior vena cava

Pulmonary artery

Aortic semilunar valve

Right atrium

Tricuspid valve

Right ventricle

Inferior vena cava

Aorta

Pulmonary semilunar valve

Pulmonary veins

Left atrium

Bicuspid (mitral) valve

Left ventricle

1 Deoxygenated blood from the body is carried by the venae cavae into the right atrium.

2 The right atrium contracts, pushing blood through the tricuspid valve into the right ventricle.

3 The right ventricle contracts, pushing blood through the pulmonary semilunar valve into the pulmonary artery.

4 The blood travels to the lungs, where carbon dioxide is exchanged for oxygen from the air.

5 Oxygenated blood from the lungs is carried by the pulmonary veins into the left atrium.

6 The left atrium contracts, pushing blood through the bicuspid valve into the left ventricle.

7 The left ventricle contracts, pushing blood through the aortic semilunar valve into the aorta.

8 The aorta delivers oxygenated blood to the body, where it is used for energy production.

The heart pumps blood around the body in a double circulatory system.

- The **pulmonary circuit** carries deoxygenated blood away from the heart to the lungs and returns oxygenated (oxygen-rich) blood to the heart.

- The **systemic circuit** carries oxygenated blood away from the heart to the body and returns deoxygenated blood to the heart.

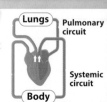

Lungs — Pulmonary circuit

Systemic circuit

Body

daydream EDUCATION

The circulatory system consists of the heart, blood vessels and blood. It is responsible for circulating blood and transporting oxygen, carbon dioxide and nutrients around the body.

Controlling Heart Rate

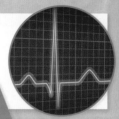

The rate at which the heart beats is controlled by a group of cells in the wall of the right atrium. This is referred to as the heart's pacemaker. Whenever extra oxygen is needed by the tissues (e.g. during exercise), the pacemaker cells will increase the heart rate so that oxygen can be pumped around the body faster.

Sometimes the pacemaker can develop a fault or be damaged. In such cases, it is possible to have surgery to fit an artificial pacemaker – an electrical device, which corrects any irregularities in the heart rate.

Blood Vessels

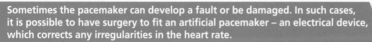

Arteries

- Carry oxygenated blood (except pulmonary artery) at high pressure, from the heart to the body

- Have thick walls made of elastic fibres

- Have narrow channels (lumen) to maintain high pressure

Veins

- Carry deoxygenated blood (except pulmonary veins) at low pressure, from the body to the heart

- Have thin walls and contain valves that prevent the backflow of blood

- Have wide channels (lumen) to ease the flow of blood

Capillaries

- Allow the exchange of materials between tissues and blood

- Have walls that are only one cell thick

- Have channels (lumen) the width of one blood cell, which distort the cells and aid gaseous exchange

Blood

Plasma

Plasma is the fluid part of blood that carries the other components (platelets, red blood cells and white blood cells) throughout the body. It also carries dissolved nutrients and carbon dioxide.

Platelets

Platelets are tiny cell fragments that clump together to help blood clot and to stop bleeding.

Red Blood Cells

Red blood cells transport oxygen from the lungs to the body's cells. They have no nucleus so that there is more space for haemoglobin, which carries oxygen. Also, the biconcave shape of these cells provides a large surface area to volume ratio for gaseous exchange.

White Blood Cells

There are different types of white blood cells, all of which contain a nucleus. One type, lymphocytes, produce antibodies that destroy pathogens. Another type, phagocytes, ingest pathogens and release enzymes to destroy them.

The Lungs and Gas Exchange

The respiratory system delivers oxygen to the circulatory system and removes carbon dioxide from the body. The circulatory system delivers carbon dioxide to the lungs and carries oxygen away to the body.

The Gaseous Exchange System in Humans

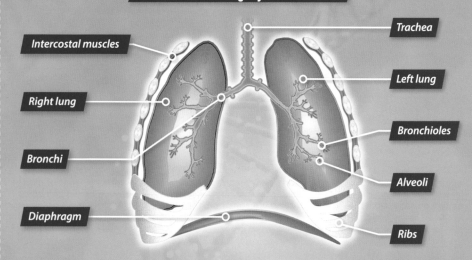

Trachea

Intercostal muscles

Right lung

Bronchi

Diaphragm

Left lung

Bronchioles

Alveoli

Ribs

The Alveoli

The lungs contain millions of alveoli that, combined, provide a large surface area.

Their walls are one single epithelial cell thick and provide a thin, permeable surface for gas exchange.

Alveoli are moist to ease gaseous diffusion.

Oxygen diffuses from the air to the blood, and carbon dioxide diffuses from the blood to the air. Diffusion occurs along steep concentration gradients.

The alveoli are rich in blood supply.

Alveoli contain phagocyte cells that destroy any bacteria not trapped by mucus in the bronchi and trachea.

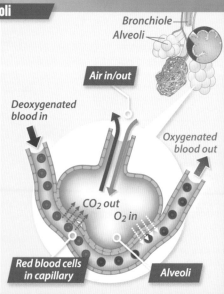

Bronchiole
Alveoli

Air in/out

Deoxygenated blood in

Oxygenated blood out

CO_2 out
O_2 in

Red blood cells in capillary

Alveoli

daydream EDUCATION

Cardiovascular Disease

Cardiovascular diseases are diseases of the heart and blood vessels.

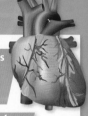

Coronary Heart Disease

Coronary arteries supply the heart muscle with blood. In coronary heart disease, layers of fatty material build up in the walls of the coronary arteries, causing their channels to narrow and reducing blood supply to the heart. The reduced flow of oxygen-rich blood through the arteries can damage cells and eventually lead to a heart attack.

Healthy Artery

Plaque Build-up

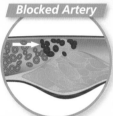

Blocked Artery

The fatty material is made of fat, cholesterol and calcium. It is more likely to build up in people who are overweight or obese and/or who have a diet high in cholesterol.

Treatments for Coronary Heart Disease

There are a number of different treatments for coronary heart disease, depending on the stage and severity of the disease.

- Sections of blocked arteries can be replaced through surgery.
- A plastic or metal mesh tube called a stent can be inserted into a blocked artery to keep it open.
- Patients can be placed on drugs called statins, which reduce blood cholesterol and therefore slow the build-up of fatty materials.
- In severe cases, a heart transplant can be performed.

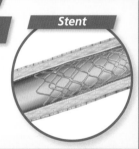

Stent

A healthy diet and active lifestyle can reduce the risk of coronary heart disease.

Faulty Heart Valves

In some people, heart valves may become damaged, reducing the efficiency of blood flow in the heart. This can cause tiredness, breathlessness and chest pains.

Faulty valves can be replaced with transplanted (biological) or artificial (mechanical) valves.

Heart Failure

When a person's heart stops beating, a heart, or heart and lung, transplant is required. This is where a heart from a matching donor is transplanted into the patient.

A donor is not always easy to find so as a temporary measure, patients can be attached to an artificial heart while they await a transplant.

Coronary heart disease is a non-communicable disease – a medical condition or disease that is not caused by infectious agents and can therefore not be passed from person to person.

Health

Health is defined as the state of physical and mental well-being. Both communicable and non-communicable diseases are major causes of ill health. Other important factors include diet, stress and life situations.

Health and Disease

Communicable Diseases

Non-Communicable Diseases

Communicable diseases are infectious; they can be spread from person to person through pathogens, such as viruses and bacteria.

Non-communicable diseases are caused by non-infectious agents and therefore cannot be passed from person to person.

Examples: influenza (flu), chicken pox and measles

Examples: cancer, dementia and diabetes

Different types of disease may interact to cause health problems.

- Immune system defects can increase the risk of catching infectious diseases.
- Viral infections can trigger some types of cancers.
- Immune reactions to a pathogen can set off allergies such as asthma.
- Severe physical illnesses can lead to mental health issues such as depression.

Lifestyle and Non-Communicable Diseases

There are various risk factors that are linked to an increased rate of a disease. People's lifestyles and their surrounding environment can have a significant impact on their health.

In some but not all cases, there is a direct link between the risk factor and the disease. However, many diseases are caused by interactions of several factors, so it is difficult to identify direct causation.

Smoking causes an increased risk of lung disease, lung cancer, mouth cancer, cardiovascular disease and damage to unborn babies.

Poor diet and obesity can cause various health problems including, cardiovascular disease, type 2 diabetes and various cancers.

daydream EDUCATION

Lifestyle and Non-Communicable Diseases Continued

Lack of exercise can lead to various health problems, which are linked to an increased risk of cardiovascular disease.

Drinking excess alcohol can directly cause an increased risk of liver disease, reduced brain function and damage to unborn babies.

Radiation and exposure to certain chemicals can directly cause certain cancers. Cancer-causing substances are called carcinogens.

A balanced diet and exercising regularly will help reduce the risk of ill health. If you are experiencing any physical or mental difficulties always seek medical help.

Cost of Non-Communicable Diseases

Non-communicable diseases have significant human and financial costs. Individuals with non-communicable diseases may have a low quality of life and a lower than average life expectancy. They may also require support from family and friends.

On a national and global scale, the cost of non-communicable diseases is huge, with billions of pounds being spent annually on researching and treating the diseases.

Cancer

Cancer is caused by changes in cells that lead to the uncontrolled growth and division of cells. The resulting mass of cells is known as a tumour. However, not all tumours are cancerous.

Benign Tumours

Benign tumours are growths of abnormal cells that are contained in one area, usually surrounded by a membrane.

These tumours are not cancerous and do not invade other parts of the body. However, they can be very large and unsightly, so they are often surgically removed.

Malignant Tumours

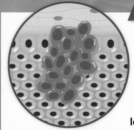

Malignant tumours spread and invade neighbouring tissues. If the cells get into the blood, they can be carried around the body, leading to secondary tumours in other organs.

These tumours are cancerous and very dangerous, so they require prompt medical treatment to prevent the cancer spreading.

Symptoms of Cancer

There are over 200 types of cancer, each of which has its own specific symptoms. However, there are several common symptoms to look out for.

If you have any of these symptoms or are worried that you may have cancer, visit your doctor immediately.

Symptoms

- ✓ Lumps on or below the surface of the skin
- ✓ Unexplainable weight loss
- ✓ Bleeding
- ✓ Coughing and breathlessness
- ✓ Changes in bowel habits

Cancer and Lifestyle

Anyone can develop cancer. However, scientists have identified several lifestyle factors that can increase the risk of developing different cancers.

Smoking	This is linked to over 1 in 5 cancer deaths in the UK.
UV Exposure	UV radiation is a major risk factor for most skin cancers.
Alcohol	This is linked to several cancers, including bowel and mouth.
Obesity	Obesity is the second largest preventable cause of cancer in the UK.
Infections	Infections such as hepatitis C can cause changes in cells and eventually lead to cancer. They can also damage the immune system.

Additionally, there are genetic risk factors for some cancers. For example, mutations in inherited *BRCA* genes are linked to an increased likelihood of developing breast cancer.

daydream EDUCATION

Plant Tissues, Organs & Systems

Just like animal cells, plant cells are organised into tissues, organs and organ systems.

Plant Tissues

Plant tissues are made up of plant cells with a similar structure and function.

Epidermal Tissue	**A single layer of cells that covers the whole plant (epidermis)**
Xylem	**Found in roots, stems and leaves; gives support and transports water and minerals**
Phloem	**Found in roots, stems and leaves; transports sugars**
Spongy Mesophyll	**Found in leaves; helps facilitate gas exchange**
Palisade Mesophyll	**Found in leaves; the main site of photosynthesis**
Meristem Tissue	**Found at the tips of roots and shoots; enables the plant to grow**

Plant Organs

Plant organs are collections of plant tissues that perform specific functions.
The three main plant organs are the root, stem and leaf.

The function of the leaf is to convert carbon dioxide and water into sugar by using light energy.

Epidermis

The lower epidermis contains pores called stomata that can open to allow carbon dioxide into the leaf. The upper epidermis is transparent to allow sunlight to pass through to the palisade layer. It also helps protect against water loss.

Palisade Mesophyll

The elongated cells in the palisade mesophyll are closely packed with many chloroplasts to absorb light energy and perform photosynthesis.

Spongy Mesophyll

Spongy mesophyll cells contain chloroplasts, but they are loosely arranged with many air spaces to allow carbon dioxide to travel up to the palisade layer.

Veins

The veins contain two tissues; xylem, which transports water to the leaf, and phloem, which transports the sugar made by photosynthesis around the plant.

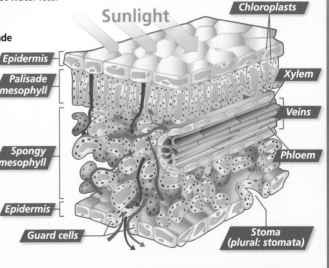

Sunlight

Chloroplasts

Epidermis
Palisade mesophyll
Spongy mesophyll
Epidermis
Guard cells

Xylem
Veins
Phloem
Stoma (plural: stomata)

| | Carbon dioxide | | Oxygen | | Water |

daydream
EDUCATION

Plant Transport

Stomata

Stomata are tiny pores that control gas exchange and water loss. They allow carbon dioxide to diffuse into the leaves and oxygen to diffuse out, along with water vapour. The stomata are surrounded by guard cells. The stomata open when the cells fill with water and become turgid; they close when the cells lose water and become flaccid.

During transpiration, water vapour diffuses out of a plant through its leaves because there is more water inside the plant than outside it. This water then needs to be replaced so more water is drawn up through the xylem vessels.

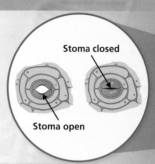

Stoma closed

Stoma open

Xylem Tissue

During their development, xylem cells die, and their top and bottom walls disintegrate to form long vessels, which are supported by a material called lignin. The vessels transport water and dissolved mineral ions from a plant's roots to its stems and leaves.

Inside xylem vessels, there is an unbroken chain of water. As the water evaporates out of the leaves through the stomata, more water is pulled up the xylem vessels to replace the water lost through evaporation.

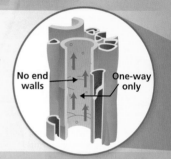

No end walls

One-way only

Phloem Tissue

Phloem is made of columns of elongated cells. These cells transport sugars made in the leaves to other parts of the plant for immediate use or storage. Phloem vessels have pores in the ends of their walls that allow food to move between them.

Phloem is not part of the transpiration process. It is used for translocation.

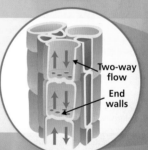

Two-way flow

End walls

Root Hair Cells

Millions of specialised root hair cells are located on the surface of plant roots. These cells stick out into the soil to provide the plant with a large surface area to absorb more water and mineral ions.

Because the concentration of minerals is greater in the root hair cells than in the surrounding soil, the plant uses active transport to absorb minerals from an area of lower concentration to an area of higher concentration.

To ensure there is a constant stream of water through the plant, any water flowing out of the xylem must be replaced by water from the roots.

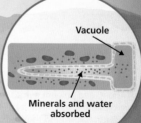

Vacuole

Minerals and water absorbed

daydream
EDUCATION

Plants are made of specialised cells, tissues and organs that work together to allow substances to move around the plant.

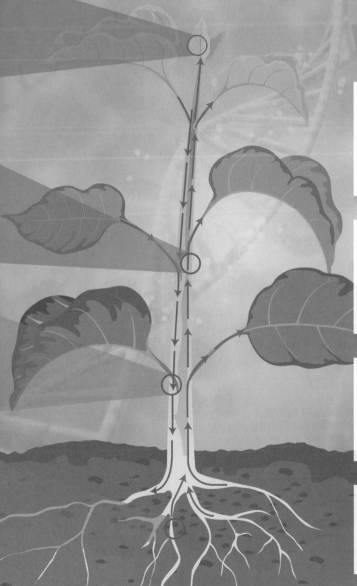

Transpiration

Transpiration is the process by which moisture is transported through a plant, from its roots to the small pores on the underside of its leaves. From the leaves, it is released into the atmosphere through evaporation and diffusion.

Translocation

Translocation is the process by which food substances, such as sucrose and amino acids, are transported through a plant.

Factors Affecting the Rate of Transpiration

Light Intensity

The greater the light intensity, the greater the rate of transpiration. When it is dark, photosynthesis cannot take place, and the stomata close. This means that little water can diffuse out of the leaves.

Temperature

The greater the temperature, the greater the rate of transpiration. Water particles have more energy when it is warm, and they evaporate and diffuse out of the stomata at a faster rate.

Air Flow

The greater the air flow, the greater the rate of transpiration. When air flow is fast, water vapour is moved away quickly to create a high concentration gradient for diffusion.

Humidity

The lower the humidity, the faster the rate of transpiration. When the air is dry, there is a high concentration gradient for diffusion.

Communicable Diseases

Bacteria

Bacteria are microscopic living cells. Some bacteria are helpful and protect against disease, whereas others, such as pathogenic bacteria, are harmful and cause disease. Pathogenic bacteria can release poisonous toxins that damage cells and make people feel ill.

The Growth of Bacteria

Bacterial cells reproduce asexually through a process called binary fission. In binary fission, a cell splits into two genetically identical daughter cells. Bacteria can reproduce rapidly in the right conditions. Most bacteria thrive in warm, moist environments that have a good source of nutrients.

Bacterial Diseases

Salmonella

Salmonella is spread by bacteria ingested in food or on food prepared in unhygienic conditions.

Symptoms include vomiting, fever, abdominal cramps and diarrhoea and are caused by the toxins the bacteria produce. In the UK, poultry is vaccinated against salmonella to control the spread.

Gonorrhoea

Gonorrhoea is a sexually transmitted disease (STD) that causes pain when urinating and a thick yellow or green discharge from the penis or vagina.

It used to be easily treated with the antibiotic penicillin, but new drug-resistant strains of the bacteria have made treatment harder. Infection can be prevented by using barrier contraception such as condoms.

Protist Diseases

Malaria

Protists are single-celled organisms, some of which are pathogens. Malaria is a serious disease that causes episodes of fever, and it can be fatal. The pathogen that causes malaria is transmitted by mosquitos. Mosquitos pick up the pathogen when they feed on infected organisms and then transmit the disease to other organisms through their saliva when they bite.

The spread of malaria is controlled by preventing mosquitos from breeding and by using mosquito nets to avoid being bitten.

Fungal Diseases

Rose Black Spot

Rose black spot is a fungus that causes purple or black spots to develop on leaves, which often turn yellow and fall off. This reduces photosynthesis and growth.

The fungal spores are spread by water and wind. Rose black spot is treated using fungicides, and the spread can be avoided by removing and destroying affected leaves.

Fungi can also cause disease in animals, such as athlete's foot and ringworm in humans.

daydream
EDUCATION

Pathogens are microorganisms (viruses, bacteria, fungi or protists) that cause communicable (infectious and contagious) disease. They infect plants or animals and can be spread through air, water, food and direct contact.

Viruses

Viruses are smaller than bacteria and harder to detect by the body's defences because they are hidden inside cells. Viruses inject their genes into a host cell and use the cell to produce thousands of copies of themselves. These copies fill the cell until it bursts, releasing the virus into the body.

Viral Diseases

Measles

Measles is a serious illness that can be fatal if complications arise. As a result, most young children are vaccinated against it.

The measles virus is spread through the inhalation of droplets from sneezes and coughs of infected people. Symptoms include fever and a red skin rash.

HIV

HIV is a virus that causes the disease AIDS. It can initially cause flu-like symptoms, but after this, there are usually no other symptoms for several years. The virus attacks the immune system, but this can be controlled by using antiretroviral drugs.

Late-stage HIV, or AIDS, develops once the immune system is so badly damaged that it cannot cope with other infections or cancers. HIV is spread through the exchange of bodily fluids, often during sex or through the sharing of needles by drug users.

TMV

Tobacco mosaic virus (TMV) is a widespread plant pathogen. It affects many different plants including tomato plants.

Its symptoms include a distinctive 'mosaic' pattern of discoloration on the leaves, which limits photosynthesis and therefore affects the growth of the plant.

Fighting Disease

The Human Defence System

The body has several ways of defending itself against pathogens.

Eyes – Tears remove unwanted particles and contain an enzyme that can kill bacteria.

Skin – Skin is difficult to penetrate, and skin cells produce oils that can kill microbes.

Nose – Mucus in the nose traps microbes, which are removed by sneezing or blowing the nose. Hairs also stop large particles containing pathogens from entering the lungs.

White Blood Cells – White blood cells protect the body from infections.

Trachea and Bronchi – The trachea and bronchi produce mucus to trap microbes, which are then carried out of the body by tiny hairs known as cilia.

Stomach – The stomach contains hydrochloric acid and enzymes that can kill microbes that enter the body through food and drink.

Blood Clotting – Microbes can enter the body through open wounds. Blood cells, known as platelets, help blood clot quickly and seal wounds to reduce the risk of infection.

White Blood Cells

1. **Ingestion** – White blood cells (phagocytes) engulf pathogens and then digest them. This process is called phagocytosis.

2. **Producing Antibodies** – Antibodies are produced by specialised white blood cells (**lymphocytes**) when they detect **antigens**, a protein found on the surface of pathogens. The antibodies, which are specific to the **antigen** detected, then find and destroy the pathogen. Some white blood cells (**memory cells**) remain in the blood. Therefore, if the same pathogen enters the body again, the antibodies to kill it can be produced quickly.

3. **Producing Antitoxins** – Some white blood cells produce proteins called antitoxins that neutralise the toxins released by pathogens.

daydream EDUCATION

Vaccinations

Vaccinations are used to protect against infections. They involve injecting a small amount of dead or inactive pathogens into the body. These harmless pathogens contain antigens that provoke white blood cells to produce antibodies to destroy them, while producing memory cells which remain in the blood.

If the same pathogen infects the body again, the memory cells recognise it and produce the appropriate antibodies to help to destroy it. As the pathogens in a vaccine are inactive and do not reproduce, they often do not produce enough memory cells to provide full immunity.

As a result, booster injections are often required to increase the number of memory cells.

Advantages

- Vaccinations prevent lots of people from contracting infectious diseases such as polio and measles.
- Epidemics can be prevented by vaccinating a large percentage of the population.

Disadvantages

- Vaccinations do not guarantee immunity to the illness in the future.
- People can experience side effects from vaccinations such as swelling, high temperatures and rashes. More serious reactions such as seizures are very rare.

Antibiotics

Antibiotics reduce the growth of bacteria without killing the body's cells. Each type of bacteria requires a different antibiotic. Therefore, if you are prescribed the wrong antibiotic, it will not work.

Antibiotics cannot destroy viruses because they reproduce inside the body's own cells. This makes it difficult to develop drugs that can kill viruses without destroying the body's cells.

Resistance

Mutation can cause bacteria to become resistant to antibiotics, resulting in more serious infections. Doctors try to avoid overprescribing antibiotics to reduce the risk of resistance. Failure to complete a full course of antibiotics can also increase the risk of resistance.

Painkillers

Many different drugs, such as aspirin and paracetamol, act as painkillers. These have no affect on pathogens but can be used to treat the symptoms of a disease. Painkillers, like all drugs, usually have some side effects.

Developing New Drugs

Traditionally, drugs have been extracted from plants and microorganisms.

The heart drug digitalis originates from foxgloves.

The painkiller aspirin originates from willow.

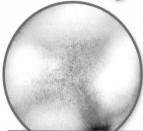

Penicillin originates from the *penicillium* mould.

Most new drugs are synthesised by chemists. However, the starting point may still be a chemical extracted from a plant. New medical drugs have to be tested and trialled before being used.

Preclinical Testing

Preclinical testing is performed in a laboratory using human cells and tissues. However, testing on cells and tissues is ineffective for a drug that affects whole or multiple organ systems. Because of this, the drug then needs to be tested on animals to identify how it works, its toxicity and the best dosage. If animal tests are successful, the drug is then tested on human volunteers in clinical trials.

- At the start of a clinical trial, a very low dose of the drug is given to healthy volunteers to identify if it has any harmful side effects. The dose is gradually increased.

- If the test results are good, the drug is tested on people who have the illness to find the optimum dose.

- Patients are split into two groups: the test group, which is given the new drug, and the control group, which is given a placebo (a substance that does not have any physical effect). Any changes to the patients' condition are monitored. If changes are only seen in the test group, the scientists know that the drug works.

- Clinical trials are performed either blind, meaning patients do not know which group they are in, or double-blind, meaning neither the doctors nor patients know. This is to remove any bias that may affect the results of the trial.

daydream EDUCATION

Photosynthesis

Photosynthesis is the process by which plants, algae and other organisms produce their own food (glucose). It is an endothermic reaction that uses light energy, carbon dioxide and water to produce glucose and oxygen.

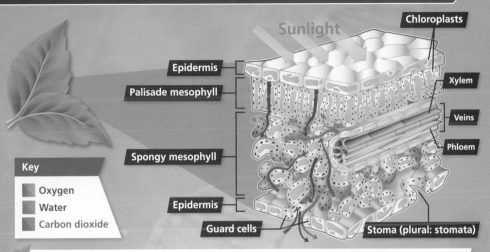

Sunlight

Chloroplasts

Epidermis

Palisade mesophyll

Xylem

Veins

Phloem

Spongy mesophyll

Epidermis

Guard cells

Stoma (plural: stomata)

Key

- Oxygen
- Water
- Carbon dioxide

1 Sunlight is absorbed by chlorophyll, a green pigment within the chloroplasts.

2 Water enters a plant through its roots by osmosis and then travels to the leaves through tubes called xylem vessels.

3 Carbon dioxide from the air diffuses into leaves through the stomata. Guard cells surrounding the stomata control their size depending on the amount of light being received.

4 Photosynthesis takes place in the chloroplasts. Light energy is used to convert water and carbon dioxide into glucose and oxygen.

5 Oxygen, a by-product of photosynthesis, leaves the plant through the stomata.

Leaves are broad and flat to provide a large surface area for the absorption of light. They are also thin, which means that carbon dioxide does not have far to diffuse into the leaf.

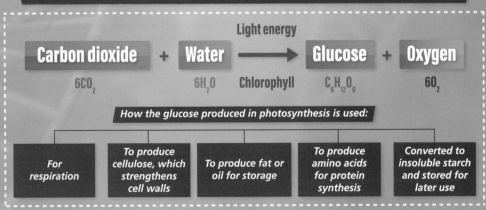

Light energy

Carbon dioxide + **Water** $\longrightarrow$ **Glucose** + **Oxygen**

$6CO_2$ $\quad$ $6H_2O$ $\quad$ Chlorophyll $\quad$ $C_6H_{12}O_6$ $\quad$ $6O_2$

How the glucose produced in photosynthesis is used:

For respiration	To produce cellulose, which strengthens cell walls	To produce fat or oil for storage	To produce amino acids for protein synthesis	Converted to insoluble starch and stored for later use

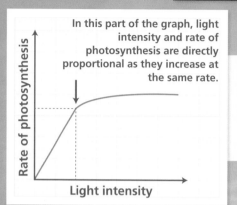

In this part of the graph, light intensity and rate of photosynthesis are directly proportional as they increase at the same rate.

Light Intensity

Increasing light intensity boosts the rate of photosynthesis to a certain level. Beyond this, other factors, such as temperature and carbon dioxide, limit the rate.

Temperature

Photosynthesis will not take place if the temperature is below approximately 0°C or above 45°C. This is because the reactions involved are catalysed by enzymes.

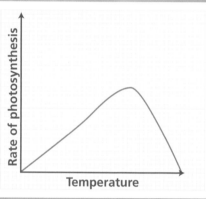

Carbon Dioxide Concentration

Increasing carbon dioxide concentration boosts the rate of photosynthesis to a certain level. Beyond this, other factors such as light intensity and temperature, limit the rate.

Chlorophyll can also limit photosynthesis. If chloroplasts become damaged through disease or lack of nutrients, they cannot absorb as much light, reducing photosynthesis. All of the above factors interact so any one factor, or multiple factors, may be responsible for limiting photosynthesis.

daydream
EDUCATION

Light Distance and Light Intensity

The light intensity in photosynthesis experiments is often measured as the light's distance from the plant. In such cases, the light intensity is inversely proportional to the square of the distance, according to the inverse square law:

$$\text{Intensity} \propto \frac{1}{\text{Distance}^2}$$

The Economics of Limiting Factors

To maximise photosynthesis in plants for food production, plants are often grown in a greenhouse, so the limiting factors can be manipulated and kept to an optimum level.

However, creating optimum levels is difficult and costs money, so it is important that each factor is adjusted only when it is limiting.

Practical Activity

The effect of light intensity on the rate of photosynthesis can be investigated using an aquatic organism, such as pondweed.

1 Cut a piece of elodea pondweed and place it upside down (cut tip facing up) into a boiling tube filled with water so it is completely submerged. Place the tube into a beaker of water which will absorb any heat from the lamp and keep the temperature around the pondweed constant.

2 Set up a lamp at a fixed distance from the pondweed.

3 Count how many bubbles the pondweed produces over a set period of time, e.g. 1 minute.

4 Repeat this two more times and calculate the mean across the three results.

5 Now repeat the experiment with the lamp at different distances from the pondweed.

If the number of bubbles increases, the pondweed is producing more oxygen, which means it is photosynthesising faster. Conversely, fewer bubbles means less oxygen and a slower rate of photosynthesis.

During an experiment, it is important to keep all control variables the same. In this experiment, carbon dioxide concentration and temperature need to remain constant.

daydream
EDUCATION

Respiration

Respiration is an exothermic reaction that occurs in living cells to release energy stored in glucose. The energy released supplies all the energy needed for living processes.

Organisms need energy for:

Movement

Chemical reactions to build larger molecules from smaller ones

Keeping warm

Aerobic Respiration (Respiration With Oxygen)

In aerobic respiration, oxygen and glucose are used to generate energy.

Glucose + **Oxygen** → **Carbon Dioxide** + **Water** + **Energy**

$C_6H_{12}O_6$ $6O_2$ $6CO_2$ $6H_2O$

Glucose is broken down to produce carbon dioxide and water, and to release energy.

Anaerobic Respiration (Respiration Without Oxygen)

In animals, anaerobic respiration takes places when the body is unable to supply muscles with sufficient oxygen for aerobic respiration.

Glucose → **Lactic Acid** + **Energy**

Glucose is broken down to produce lactic acid and to release energy.

In plant cells, anaerobic respiration takes place when there is insufficient oxygen for plants to respire aerobically.

Glucose → **Ethanol** + **Carbon Dioxide** + **Energy**

Glucose is broken down to produce ethanol (an alcohol) and carbon dioxide, and to release energy.

Anaerobic respiration does not release as much energy as aerobic respiration because the oxidation of glucose is not completed – that is, the glucose is not fully broken down.

Anaerobic Respiration in Yeast

Anaerobic respiration in yeast is called fermentation. Yeast is a fungus, but it respires in the same way as plants do. It is used commercially in the manufacture of bread and alcoholic drinks.

daydream EDUCATION

Exercise and Metabolism

Exercise

During exercise, the body reacts to the increased demand for energy.

Breathing rate and breath volume increase to get more oxygen into the blood and to remove carbon dioxide.

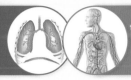

Heart rate also increases to get oxygenated blood to the muscles more rapidly and to remove more carbon dioxide.

During vigorous exercise, the body may be unable to supply the muscles with sufficient oxygen for aerobic respiration. As a result, the muscles also respire anaerobically, and the incomplete oxidation of glucose causes a build up of lactic acid (causing muscle fatigue) and creates an oxygen debt.

REST   EXERCISE   RECOVERY

OXYGEN DEFICIT

OXYGEN CONSUMPTION

OXYGEN DEBT

TIME

To repay oxygen debt, extra oxygen must be taken on after anaerobic exercise to convert lactic acid into waste products (carbon dioxide and water) that can be removed from the body.

Lactic acid is also transported in the blood to the liver, where it is converted back into glucose.

After exercise, we take deeper or quicker breaths to take in more oxygen and remove more carbon dioxide. Long periods of vigorous activity result in muscles becoming fatigued and then contracting less efficiently.

Metabolism

Metabolism is the sum of all the reactions taking place in a living organism. These reactions are controlled by enzymes and use energy from respiration either to break down large molecules into smaller molecules or to synthesise (make) large molecules from smaller ones.

Carbohydrates

- Broken down into simple sugars, including glucose

- Built up into starch and cellulose (in plants) or glycogen (in animals)

Proteins

- Broken down into amino acids*

- Glucose and nitrate ions form amino acids, which are built up into proteins.

Lipids (fats)

- Broken down into glycerol and fatty acids

- Built up into lipids. It takes a molecule of glycerol and three fatty acid molecules to form a lipid molecule.

*Animals cannot store protein, so excess protein is broken down into urea and excreted from the body in urine.

Respiration is a series of reactions. Although respiration releases energy overall, some of the reactions also require energy.

Homeostasis

Cells can survive only within narrow physical and chemical limits. Homeostasis is the regulation of the conditions within the body to maintain optimal conditions for enzyme action and other cell functions. In the body, homeostasis controls:

 Body temperature   **Blood glucose concentration**   **Water levels**

Control Systems

There are various control systems in the body, all of which include:

Receptors	Coordination Centres	Effectors

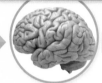

Groups of specialist cells that detect stimuli (changes in the environment).	Receive information and coordinate any possible response.	Bring about responses to restore optimum conditions.
Light receptor cells in the eye	*Brain, spinal cord, pancreas*	*Muscles or glands*

Negative Feedback

Negative feedback is a control mechanism used in homeostasis that maintains optimum conditions within a system. It occurs when a change from normal conditions in the body leads to a series of events that reverse the change.

Example: Body Temperature Control

Receptors	Control Centre	Effectors
Receptors in the skin and brain detect a rise in body temperature to over 37°C.	*The brain activates heat loss response.*	*Sweat glands secrete sweat, and blood vessels close to the skin dilate in order to lose heat and reduce body temperature.*

 BODY TEMP > 37°C

BODY TEMPERATURE = 37°C

BODY TEMP < 37°C

Effectors	Control Centre	Receptors
Muscles shiver to increase body temperature, and blood vessels close to the skin constrict to reduce heat loss.	*The brain activates heat retention response.*	*Receptors in the skin and brain detect a fall in body temperature to below 37°C.*

daydream EDUCATION

The Endocrine System

The endocrine system is made up of glands that secrete hormones into the bloodstream.

Hormones are chemical 'messengers' that travel in the bloodstream from their source to target organs, where they produce an effect. Their effect is slower than that of the nervous system. However, they can target several different locations, and their effects act for longer.

Main Endocrine Glands in the Human Body

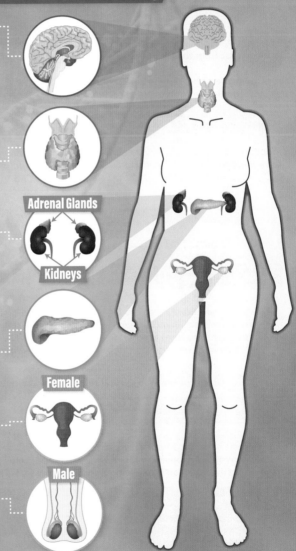

Pituitary Gland

The pituitary gland is attached to the underside of the brain. It acts like a 'master gland' because the hormones it secretes act on other glands to stimulate them to produce their own hormones. It secretes its hormones in response to changes in body conditions.

Thyroid Gland

The thyroid gland produces hormones that regulate the rate of metabolism in cells.

Adrenal Glands

The adrenal glands produce hormones that help to regulate metabolism and blood pressure. Also, in response to a perceived threat or danger, they produce adrenaline to prepare the body to either fight or flee.

Pancreas

The pancreas produces the hormones insulin and glucagon, which regulate blood sugar levels.

Ovaries

Ovaries produce the hormone oestrogen, which regulates the monthly menstrual cycle.

Testes

Testes produce the hormone testosterone, which stimulates sperm production.

Adrenal Glands

Kidneys

Female

Male

The Human Nervous System

The Human Nervous System

The nervous system enables humans to react to their environment and to coordinate their behaviour. It consists of two parts:

1 Central Nervous System (CNS), which includes the brain and spinal cord

2 Peripheral Nervous System (PNS), the network of nerves that lead out from the CNS to the rest of the body

Nerves are made of nerve cells called neurones, which carry messages in the form of electrical impulses.

Key
- ■ CNS
- ■ PNS

Brain
Spinal cord
Peripheral nerve

Sensory Neurones
Sensory neurones carry impulses from the receptor to the CNS.

Relay Neurones
Relay neurones carry impulses within the CNS.

Motor Neurones
Motor neurones carry impulses from the CNS to the effector.

The coordination of actions in the body always follows a certain sequence:

Stimulus	Receptor		Coordinator		Effector	Response
Heat	Temperature receptors	Sensory Neurones	Brain	Motor Neurones	Sweat glands	Secrete sweat

When temperature receptors in the skin detect an increase in temperature, impulses are sent to the brain along sensory neurones.

The brain coordinates a response and sends this to the sweat glands along motor neurones.

The sweat glands secrete sweat to increase heat loss by evaporation.

Other control systems and responses also regulate body temperature.

Reflex Actions

Reflex actions have two important features: they are automatic/involuntary and very rapid. They often have some sort of protective function to prevent injury. Examples include:

- Swallowing
- Blinking
- Pupil reflex
- Breathing
- Coughing
- Sneezing
- Withdrawal reflex (pulling away from a painful stimulus)

daydream EDUCATION

The Reflex Arc

In reflex actions, the nerve impulses always follow a certain pathway.

When a stimulus is detected by the receptor, impulses travel along the sensory neurones to relay neurones in the spinal cord and then out to the effector via the motor neurones.

The impulses do not go through the brain as the response needs to be automatic. However, the brain will still receive the sensory input while the reflex is being carried out.

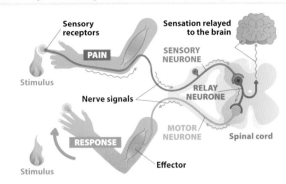

Sensory receptors

Sensation relayed to the brain

PAIN

SENSORY NEURONE

Stimulus

Nerve signals

RELAY NEURONE

MOTOR NEURONE

Spinal cord

RESPONSE

Stimulus

Effector

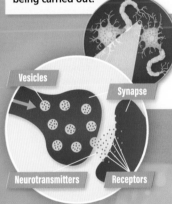

Vesicles

Synapse

Neurotransmitters

Receptors

Synapses

Synapses, the junctions between neurones, slightly delay impulses: when impulses transfer from one neurone to another across a synapse, they must be converted into chemical signals and back again.

In a reflex arc, the impulses go through only two synapses, so the delay is minimal. In the brain, the impulses would travel through millions of synapses.

Practical Activity

Reaction time is the time taken to react to a stimulus. The effects of a factor on human reaction time can be investigated using the ruler drop test.

The ruler drop test can be used to measure reaction time in response to external factors such as a visual or audio cue. The test is performed with a partner who holds the ruler.

As your partner holds the ruler, stand with your hand in front of you and position the ruler in between your index finger and thumb. The top of your index finger should be level with 0 cm on the ruler.

Your partner then drops the ruler, and you must catch the ruler as quickly as possible. Measure the point at which you caught the ruler from the top of your thumb. For improved reliability, repeat two more times, and then calculate the mean of your three scores.

Control of Blood Glucose Concentration

Glucose is needed for energy, but high levels of glucose in the blood can be harmful. Hormones from the pancreas control blood glucose concentration.

Pancreatic Hormones

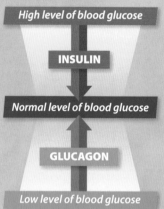

High level of blood glucose

INSULIN

Normal level of blood glucose

GLUCAGON

Low level of blood glucose

If the concentration of blood glucose gets too high, the pancreas secretes **insulin**. This triggers cells to take in glucose from the blood. The glucose is then converted into glycogen in the liver and muscles to **reduce blood glucose concentration**.

If the level of blood glucose falls too low, the pancreas produces **glucagon**. This triggers the muscles and liver to convert glycogen back into glucose. This glucose is then released into the bloodstream to **increase blood glucose concentration**.

This type of control is an example of negative feedback (see Homeostasis page for more information).

Diabetes

Diabetes is a disorder in which the body is unable to control the blood glucose level effectively. If unmanaged, diabetes can be very dangerous, leading to serious health problems.

Type 1 Diabetes

- The pancreas fails to produce sufficient insulin.
- It is characterised by uncontrolled high blood glucose and by glucose in the urine.
- It is treated with insulin injections.
- Monitoring carbohydrate intake and exercising regularly can help manage blood glucose level.
- It usually develops in children or young people.
- The cause is unknown.

Type 2 Diabetes

- The body cells no longer respond to insulin.
- It is characterised by uncontrolled high blood glucose (often not as high as in type 1) and glucose in the urine.
- Obesity is a big risk factor in the development of type 2 diabetes. As a result, it is usually treated with a carbohydrate-controlled diet and an exercise regime, along with tablets.

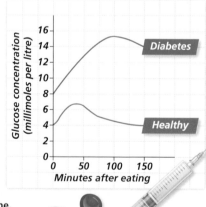

Graph: Glucose concentration (millimoles per litre) vs Minutes after eating. Y-axis values: 0, 2, 4, 6, 8, 10, 12, 14, 16. X-axis values: 0, 50, 100, 150. Curves labelled *Diabetes* and *Healthy*.

daydream EDUCATION

Hormones in Human Reproduction

The functioning of the human reproductive system is regulated by hormones in both males and females. In females, hormones control the menstrual cycle and pregnancy.

Hormones in Males and Females

♀ Females

In females, the main reproductive hormone, oestrogen, is produced by the ovaries. It helps facilitate the menstrual cycle and the development of female secondary sex characteristics.

At puberty, eggs already formed in the ovaries begin to mature, and one is released approximately every 28 days (ovulation).

Males ♂

In males, the main reproductive hormone, testosterone, is produced by the testes. Testosterone stimulates sperm development at a constant rate from puberty.

In both sexes, reproductive hormones control the development of secondary sex characteristics, such as breast development, voice breaking and body hair growth.

The Menstrual Cycle

During the menstrual cycle, an egg is released from one ovary, and the female's uterus is prepared for a possible pregnancy. If the egg is not fertilised, the uterus reverts to its original state by shedding its lining in the process of menstruation (a period, when blood is lost).

MENSTRUAL CALENDAR

5	6	7	8	9	10	11
12	13	14	15	16	17	18
19	20	21	22	23	24	25
26	27	28	29	30	31	
			1	2	3	4

The process is controlled by several different hormones.

Follicle-stimulating hormone (FSH) is released by the pituitary gland. It causes the maturation of the egg cell in the ovary and stimulates the production of oestrogen by the ovaries.

Luteinising hormone (LH) is produced by the pituitary gland and stimulates ovulation, the release of eggs from the ovaries, at 14 days.

Oestrogen and progesterone are produced in the ovaries. Both control the development and maintenance of the uterus lining in preparation for pregnancy.

FSH causes the maturation of an egg.

Oestrogen causes growth and repair of uterus lining.

Ovulation is caused by a peak in LH. During this time, there is also a fall in oestrogen.

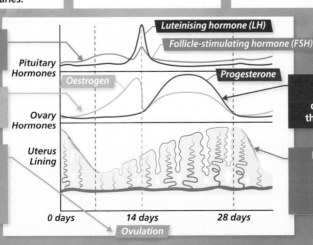

Progesterone continues the development of the uterus lining.

Menstruation is brought about by a fall in progesterone and oestrogen.

Contraception

Hormonal Methods of Contraception

Hormones are used in the natural control of fertility. Hormones can be used artificially to prevent the fertilisation of an egg by a sperm, which results in pregnancy.

Hormonal methods of contraception include:

Oral Contraceptive Pill

The oral contraceptive pill contains oestrogen and progesterone, which inhibit follicle stimulating hormone (FSH) production. In turn, this prevents the maturation of eggs and implantation if fertilisation does occur.

Progesterone

Progesterone can be injected, implanted or delivered via a skin patch to inhibit the maturation and release of eggs naturally and therefore prevents pregnancy.

Non-Hormonal Methods of Contraception

Barrier Contraception

Barrier contraception prevents sperm from reaching the egg.

Condoms are worn over the penis to stop sperm entering the vagina. They also prevent the exchange of bodily fluids so protect against most STDs.

Diaphragms are shallow plastic domes that are placed over a woman's cervix to prevent sperm from entering the uterus. They are often covered in spermicidal agents that kill or damage sperm.

Intrauterine Device

Intrauterine devices (IUDs) are T-shaped 'coils' that are inserted into the uterus to prevent the implanting of an embryo in the uterus.

Some IUDs damage sperm so they cannot reach the egg. There are also hormonal IUDs. These release hormones that can prevent the release of an egg or thicken cervical mucus so the sperm cannot reach the egg.

Sterilisation

Sterilisation is a permanent form of contraception.

Male sterilisation (vasectomy) is a surgical procedure that involves the tying or cutting of the sperm ducts between the testes and the penis.

Female sterilisation is a surgical procedure that involves the tying or cutting of the fallopian tubes between the ovaries and the uterus.

People who do not wish to use artificial contraception can prevent pregnancy by abstaining from intercourse during the times when an egg may be in the fallopian tube (oviduct). However, this is not always 100% effective.

daydream
EDUCATION

Treating Infertility

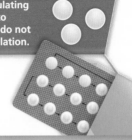

Some women produce only a small amount of follicle-stimulating hormone (FSH) and luteinising hormone (LH), which leads to reduced ovarian function. This means that ovarian follicles do not grow properly, and an egg may not be released during ovulation.

Developments in modern reproductive technology have enabled hormones to be used to treat infertility. Fertility drugs (clomiphene, taken as a pill, and FSH and LH injections) are the initial main treatment for women with ovulation disorders.

In Vitro Fertilisation (IVF)

In IVF, fertilisation occurs outside the body.

Step 1

The mother is given FSH and LH to stimulate the production of multiple eggs.

Step 2

Eggs are collected from the mother and fertilised by sperm from the father in a laboratory.

Step 3

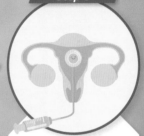

The eggs develop into early-stage embryos, and one or two are inserted into the mother's uterus.

Issues Around Fertility Treatment

Although fertility treatments enable infertile women and couples to have children, success rates are still relatively low (although improving); this can cause a lot of physical and emotional pain. There is also a greater risk of complications due to the increased chance of having multiple children.

During IVF, embryos are often destroyed. As a result, some people argue that IVF treatment is unethical and immoral because it destroys potential lives.

Adrenaline & Thyroxine

Adrenaline

Adrenaline is a hormone produced by the adrenal glands, which are found on the top of the kidneys. This hormone is produced at times of fear or stress, and prepares the body for 'fight or flight'.

- Adrenaline increases breathing rate to get more oxygen into the body.

- It also increases heart rate to pump oxygen and glucose to muscles more quickly.

- Adrenaline causes the liver to convert glycogen to glucose for increased energy.

The increased oxygen supply allows the body to respond more quickly in an emergency.

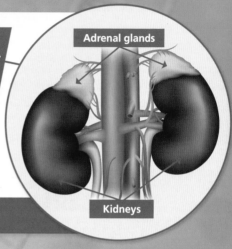

Adrenal glands

Kidneys

Larynx

Thyroid   Trachea

Thyroxine

Thyroxine is a hormone produced by the thyroid gland, which is found at the front of the trachea.

This hormone stimulates metabolism and plays an important role in growth and development. It also helps to maintain body temperature in cold conditions.

Anterior pituitary gland releases thyroid-stimulating hormone

Metabolic rate decreases

Thyroid gland releases thyroxine

Thyroxine levels are controlled by negative feedback.

Thyroid gland stops releasing thyroxine

Metabolic rate increases

Anterior pituitary gland stops releasing thyroid-stimulating hormone

daydream
EDUCATION

Reproduction

Reproduction is the process of generating offspring. There are two forms of reproduction: sexual and asexual.

Sexual Reproduction

Sexual reproduction takes place in animals and plants. It involves the joining (fusion) of male and female gametes (sex cells), which are formed through meiosis (see meiosis section for more information).

In both plants and animals, the female gamete is an egg cell. In animals, the male gamete is sperm, and in flowering plants, it is pollen.

Egg (Ovum)	Sperm	Zygote (Fertilised egg)
23 chromosomes	23 chromosomes	46 chromosomes in 23 pairs

Human cells contain 46 chromosomes (23 pairs), but gametes (egg and sperm cells) contain only half this amount (one of each pair). When the two gametes fuse together during fertilisation, a cell containing the full set of 46 chromosomes is formed. The resulting cell contains a mixture of genetic material from the mother and the father.

Which of the pair of chromosomes ends up in each gamete is random. Therefore, all of the gametes are genetically different from each other. This also creates genetic variety in the offspring.

Asexual Reproduction

Asexual reproduction occurs in plants, bacteria and other simple organisms.

New cells are formed through mitosis only.

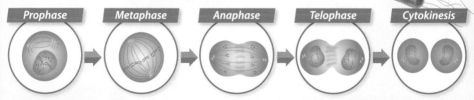

Prophase	Metaphase	Anaphase	Telophase	Cytokinesis

The cell divides to create two daughter cells, each of which has the same number of chromosomes as the parent nucleus.

Asexual reproduction involves one parent and no fusing of gametes, so there is no mixing of genetic material. Therefore, the offspring are genetically identical (clones).

Meiosis

Cells in reproductive organs divide by meiosis to form gametes.

Body cells normally divide by the process of mitosis. However, the formation of gametes requires a different form of cell division called **meiosis**. In humans, this process ensures that each gamete contains 23 chromosomes, half the amount of a normal body cell, which contains 46 chromosomes.

In meiosis, there are two divisions so four cells (two daughter cells) are created from one.

The diagram below shows the stages in meiosis in a simplified format.

1 Before a cell divides, its genetic information is duplicated, creating a chromosome that consists of two identical chromatids. This process is known as DNA replication.

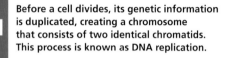

Duplication

2 The chromosomes line up in pairs at the centre of the cell (equator). The pairs are then pulled apart with half of the pair moving to one side of the cell and the other moving to the opposite side.

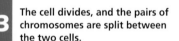

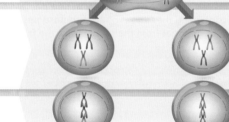

3 The cell divides, and the pairs of chromosomes are split between the two cells.

4 The chromosomes line up at the centre of the cell, and the chromatids separate to create four gametes that have a single set (half the normal number) of chromosomes.

Which half of a pair of chromosomes ends up in each gamete is random. This means that all the gametes genetically differ from each other.

Embryonic Development

When the male and female gametes fuse through fertilisation, the normal number of chromosomes is restored.

The new cell then divides by mitosis during growth into an embryo. As the embryo develops, the cells differentiate into specialised cells that make up the whole organism.

daydream EDUCATION

DNA

The genetic material in organisms is composed of a chemical called deoxyribonucleic acid, or DNA. It is found in the nucleus of animal and plant cells in structures called chromosomes.

Cell

Nucleus

The nucleus of a cell contains chromosomes, which are made of DNA molecules.

DNA

DNA contains the genetic instructions for the development and function of organisms. It is a polymer consisting of two strands that are wound into a double helix (twisted ladder shape).

The strands are made of repeating units called **nucleotides**.

Each nucleotide consists of a sugar and phosphate group linked to one of four bases: thymine (T), adenine (A), guanine (G) and cytosine (C).

These bases pair up in a specific way, known as complementary base pairing.

G **always binds to** C

Guanine   Cytosine

T **always binds to** A

Thymine   Adenine

Base
Sugar   Phosphate

Genetic Inheritance

Each human cell with a nucleus (except gametes) contains 23 pairs of chromosomes (46 in total).

In each pair, one chromosome is inherited from the person's mother and one is inherited from the father.

The chromosomes contain the genes inherited from both parents. There may be different forms of the same genes called alleles.

Genome

The genome is the entire genetic material of an organism. An understanding of the human genome is vitally important. It enables scientists to:

- Search for genes linked to different types of disease.
- Understand and treat inherited disorders.
- Trace human migration patterns from the past.

The entire human genome has been studied, and the position of every gene is now known.

Chromosomes

Genetic Mutations

Genetic mutations occur when DNA changes, altering genetic instructions. Mutations can be neutral (have no effect), improve a protein or result in a protein that does not work, which may cause a disorder.

Gene

Genes are sections of DNA in a chromosome that code for proteins.

Proteins are made of long chains of amino acids.

Genes instruct cells how to sequence amino acids to make different proteins.

Each gene codes for a particular sequence of amino acids to make a specific protein.

Each amino acid is coded by a sequence of three bases (triplet). For example, the amino acid glycine is coded by the triplet GGA.

Glycine
G
G
A

daydream
EDUCATION

Genetic Inheritance

Control Systems

Every cell in the human body, except gametes, contains 23 pairs of chromosomes. One chromosome in each pair is inherited from the mother's ovum and one is inherited from the father's sperm.

The genes that an organism inherits from its parents determine its characteristics.

Some characteristics are controlled by a single gene (e.g. fur colour in mice, red–green colour blindness in humans), but most are a result of multiple genes interacting (e.g. height in humans).

 Variations of a given gene are called **alleles**, and **every gene has more than one allele**. Alleles operate at a molecular level to determine the genetic makeup of an organism (genotype), and therefore, its physical (phenotypic) characteristics.

Alleles are either dominant or recessive.

A dominant allele will always be expressed, even if only one copy is present.

For example, the allele for brown eyes is dominant. Therefore, only one copy is needed to have brown eyes. (Two copies will also result in brown eyes.)

A recessive allele is not always expressed. For a recessive allele to be expressed, two copies must be present.

For example, the allele for blue eyes is recessive. Therefore, two copies of this allele are needed to have blue eyes.

Two alleles can be equally dominant. In such cases, both alleles are expressed equally. For example, the blood group AB is the result of codominance of the A and B dominant alleles.

If the two alleles present are the same, the organism is homozygous for that trait. However, if the alleles are different, they are heterozygous.

Key Terms

Gene	A small section of DNA
Alleles	Variations of a given gene
Homozygous	Two identical alleles
Heterozygous	Two different alleles
Genotype	The genetic makeup of an individual organism (i.e. the alleles it contains)
Phenotype	The way a gene is expressed; its observable characteristics
Dominant	An allele that is always expressed in the phenotype
Recessive	An allele that shows in the phenotype only when it is homozygous

daydream
EDUCATION

Genetic Prediction Using Punnet Squares

It is possible to work out the possible genotypes of offspring using diagrams called punnet squares. In these tables, alleles are given single letter symbols. Dominant alleles are always capital letters, and recessive alleles are always lower-case letters.

The example below shows a cross that could result in a plant with red or white flowers.

Red is dominant and white is recessive. Therefore, red is the capitalised letter (R) and white is the lower-case letter (r). The same letter is always used for both alleles.

	Plant 1	Plant 2
Phenotypes	Red	Red
Genotypes	Rr	Rr
Gametes	R or r	R or r

These are the possible **gametes** that each plant can produce. A gamete has only one allele.

Although both plants are red, they are heterozygous, with red and white alleles. They have the genotype **Rr**.

The punnet square below shows all the ways in which parents' gametes can combine to produce different genotypes in the offspring.

Plant 1 *Gametes*

Plant 2 *Gametes*

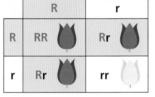

	R	r
R	RR	Rr
r	Rr	rr

The letters on the outside of the grid represent the parents' gametes. The combinations of letters inside the grid show the possible genotypes of the offspring.

Using the punnet square, you can calculate the outcomes of the cross as follows.

Outcome	Genome	Chance	Percentage
Homozygous dominant red flower	RR	1 in 4	25%
Heterozygous red flower	Rr	2 in 4	50%
Homozygous recessive white flower	rr	1 in 4	25%
Red flower	RR or Rr	3 in 4	75%
White flower	rr	1 in 4	25%

We say that the offspring have a 3:1 ratio of red to white.

The ratio indicates the probability of getting each type of plant. It is three times more likely that a red-flowered plant will be produced than a white-flowered one. It does not mean that there will always be **exactly** three times as many red-flowered plants as white-flowered ones.

Genetic inheritance can also be shown using a family tree (see Inherited Disorders section).

Inherited Disorders

Certain alleles can be harmful and cause genetic disorders. Many of these alleles are recessive, but some are dominant.

Genetic Disorders

Polydactyly (having extra fingers and toes) is a rare genetic disorder that is caused by a dominant allele.

Because the allele is dominant, it is inherited when only one parent has a defective allele. It also means that any parent with the defective gene will also have the disorder.

In the examples below, the allele for polydactyly is Y. The recessive, normal allele is y.

If one parent in a couple has polydactyly and a genotype of Yy, the offspring has a 50% chance of having the disorder (Yy).

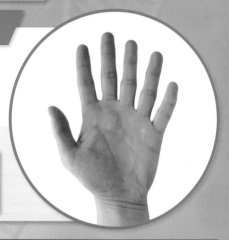

	y	y
Y	Yy	Yy
y	yy	yy

Cystic fibrosis (CF) is a disorder of the cell membrane caused by a recessive allele.

The faulty gene causes the production of thick sticky mucus which results in a wide range of health problems, including breathing problems.

Because the allele is recessive, a person with only one defective allele will not have cystic fibrosis, but they will be a carrier. To have cystic fibrosis, a person needs to inherit a defective allele from both parents.

In the examples below, the allele for cystic fibrosis is f. The dominant, normal allele is F.

One Parent Carries

	F	f
F	FF	Ff
F	FF	Ff

If only one parent is a carrier, the offspring has a 50% chance of being a carrier (Ff) but cannot have the disorder.

Both Parents Carry

	F	f
F	FF	Ff
f	Ff	ff

If both parents are carriers, the offspring has a 50% chance of being a carrier (Ff) and a 25% chance of having the disorder (ff).

One Parent with CF

	f	f
F	Ff	Ff
F	Ff	Ff

If one parent has CF and the other is not a carrier, the offspring cannot have the disorder but will definitely be a carrier (Ff).

daydream
EDUCATION

Family Trees

Family trees can be used to show how genetic disorders have been inherited in a family over multiple generations. Each generation is connected to the next by a vertical line, with the oldest generation at the top of the tree.

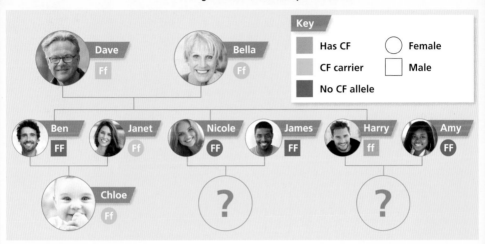

Key

■	Has CF	◯	Female
■	CF carrier	▢	Male
■	No CF allele		

Dave — Ff
Bella — Ff

Ben — FF
Janet — Ff
Nicole — FF
James — FF
Harry — ff
Amy — FF

Chloe — Ff
?
?

Dave and Bella are both carriers of cystic fibrosis, so their chance of having a child with cystic fibrosis is 25%, or 1 in 4. This does not mean that if they have four children, one will definitely have cystic fibrosis; each child's chance of having the disorder is independent.

In reality, the family tree shows that they had three children: one, Harry, with cystic fibrosis and two, Ben and Nicole, who are completely free of the defective allele.

Ben and Janet's child, Chloe, is a carrier.

As neither Nicole nor James are carriers, their children will also be free of cystic fibrosis.

Harry has cystic fibrosis. If he has a child with his non-carrier partner, Amy, their child will not have the disorder. However, it will definitely be a carrier of the defective allele.

	F	F
f	Ff	Ff
f	Ff	Ff

Embryo Screening

Embryo screening involves examining the genetic makeup of embryos to check for disorders such as cystic fibrosis or Down's syndrome.

There are many economic, social and ethical issues concerning embryo screening because it gives parents the opportunity to abort the embryo if a problem is detected. Screening is also expensive and can damage healthy embryos.

Sex Determination

In humans, ordinary body cells contain 23 pairs of chromosomes. Of these 23 pairs, 22 control characteristics only, and one carries the genes that determine sex.

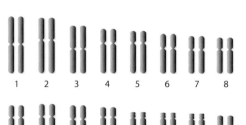

1 2 3 4 5 6 7 8

9 10 11 12 13 14 15 16

17 18 19 20 21 22   XX or XY

Female XX	Male XY

Females have two X chromosomes, so the female genotype is XX.
In males, the paired chromosomes are not identical, and the genotype is described as XY.

Gametes form from cell division during meiosis.

When the female sex chromosome pair divides, each gamete (egg) gets an X chromosome.

XX → X, X

When the male sex chromosome pair divides, each gamete (sperm) either gets an X chromosome or a Y chromosome.

XY → X, Y

Sex Inheritance

A genetic cross can be used to show sex inheritance.

		Mother gametes	
		X	X
Father gametes	X	XX	XX
	Y	XY	XY

The genetic cross shows that there is an equal chance of having a boy or girl.

There is a 50% (2 in 4) chance of having a boy (XY).

There is a 50% (2 in 4) chance of having a girl (XX).

daydream EDUCATION

Variation

Populations of living organisms show extensive variation, with all organisms displaying different characteristics.

What Causes Variation?

The phenotype of an organism is determined by a combination of its genotype (genetic makeup) and how it interacts with the environment.

Even within the same species and breed, there is variation. For example, no two humans are genetically identical.

Genetic Factors

Variation is caused by differences in genes inherited from parents' genotypes.

Examples: blood group, fur colour, leaf shape

Combination of Factors

Some variations are caused by an interaction of genetics and the environment.

Examples: weight, skin colour, plant height

Environmental Factors

Variation is caused by environmental influences or interactions with the environment.

Examples: piercings, scars, leaf discolouration

Mutations and the Origin of Variety

All genetic variations in a population originate from past mutations (changes in DNA).

Mutations occur naturally and continually, and most have little to no effect on the organism's phenotype. However, some mutations do influence the phenotype, either causing harm or improvement, but very rarely does a mutation produce a completely new phenotype.

If a mutation benefits the survival chances of an organism, it can lead to a relatively rapid change in the species. For example, if the new phenotype is suited to a change in the environment, it can lead to rapid change.

Mutations can also be caused by outside factors, such as certain chemicals and radiation.

Evolution

Over time, the inherited characteristics of a population change through the process of natural selection. This may eventually lead to the formation of a new species.

The theory of evolution by natural selection states that all species have evolved from simple life forms that first developed more than three billion years ago. It was first formulated by Charles Darwin in 1859.

Natural Selection

Natural selection is the theory that individuals best adapted to their environment are likely to outcompete those less adapted to survive. They are also likely to produce more offspring.

- Mutations result in variations in the population.
- Some phenotypes have an increased chance of survival.
- More of the phenotypes best suited to the environment will survive to breed, passing on the advantageous alleles.
- A greater proportion of the next generation will have the advantageous phenotype.
- The process repeats generation after generation, making the advantageous phenotype more and more common.

Example of Natural Selection

Over time, giraffes evolved longer necks and legs to increase their chance of survival.

1 There are giraffes with varying neck and leg lengths in a population.

2 The giraffes with longer necks and legs can reach food that is higher up. Therefore, they have a greater chance of survival.

3 Shorter giraffes have less chance of survival so fewer remain in the population and reproduce. Conversely, more taller giraffes remain to produce offspring with the more desirable traits in their phenotype.

4 A greater proportion of the taller giraffes remain in the population generation after generation, making the better phenotype more and more common.

Evolution of New Species

A species is a group of organisms that can successfully breed with each other to produce fertile offspring.

Sometimes, evolution causes populations within a species to become so different in phenotype that they can no longer interbreed to produce fertile offspring. Therefore, creating two new species. This is known as **speciation**.

daydream
EDUCATION

Selective Breeding

Selective breeding, or artificial selection, is the process by which plants and animals are bred for particular genetic characteristics.

It involves breeding organisms with desirable characteristics to produce offspring that share these characteristics. This is then repeated over multiple generations to continually improve the characteristics and spread them across the whole of the population.

Breeding Sheep for Wool

From an existing flock, males and females with the best quality wool are separated out and bred together.

Their offspring are once again assessed, and those with the best quality wool are used for breeding.

In each generation, the quality of the wool is better than the last because those with poorer quality wool have been removed from the breeding programme.

Other Examples of Selective Breeding

Crops have been bred for improved disease resistance.

Cows have been bred for either greater milk production or improved meat quality.

Plants have been bred to produce large or unusually coloured flowers.

Dogs have been bred for intelligence and a calm temperament.

Disadvantages of Selective Breeding

Animals or plants that are selectively bred are often closely related, which reduces the gene pool (the total set of genes in a population) and increases the chances of inbreeding.

As well as amplifying desirable characteristics, selective breeding can increase the chances of organisms inheriting defective genes that cause diseases and other health problems. The lack of variation in a population can also reduce resistance to new communicable diseases.

The English bulldog, which has been bred for appearance, now suffers from a wide variety of health problems due to inherited defects. Furthermore, the dogs now lack the genetic diversity needed for breeders to selectively breed unhealthy dogs with healthier phenotypes.

Genetic Engineering

Genetic engineering involves modifying the genome of an organism by inserting a gene cut out from the DNA of another organism to provide useful characteristics.

Genetically Modified Crops

Plants have been genetically engineered to be resistant to diseases or to produce bigger and better-quality crops. Plants that have been changed in this way are called genetically modified (GM) crops.

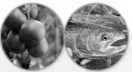

Cotton plants + genes from bacteria for toxin resistance

⬇

Cotton plants that are resistant to insect attack

⬇

Higher yields of cotton

Tomato plants + antifreeze genes from cold-water fish

⬇

Tomato plants that are resistant to frost

⬇

Tomatoes that can be grown outside in cold climates all year round

Corn plants + genes from soil bacteria for herbicide resistance

⬇

Corn plants that are resistant to herbicides

⬇

Fields that can be sprayed with herbicide and only the weeds will die

There are benefits and possible risks of GM crops.

Benefits
- Increased crop yields = more food
- Better quality food
- Reduction in use of chemical insecticides

Possible Risks
- Health risks from eating GM crops
- Reduced biodiversity caused by killing weeds and insects
- Herbicide resistance passing to weeds

Human Proteins

Bacteria can be genetically modified to produce human proteins, such as insulin, which is used to treat people with diabetes.

Human cell

Nucleus containing human DNA

Bacterial cell

1 The insulin gene is cut out of the DNA with a restriction enzyme.

2 The gene is inserted into the plasmid vector, and the ends are joined using a ligase enzyme.

3 The plasmid carries the human DNA into the bacterial cell. It is the vector.

4 The bacteria now produces the human insulin protein.

Gene Therapy

Researchers are currently investigating possible ways to cure inherited disorders (e.g. cystic fibrosis) by replacing faulty alleles in the human genome with healthy alleles.

There are ethical concerns that people may use this process to have 'designer' children with particular characteristics, such as sporting talent or high intelligence. Some people are also concerned that genetic engineering could result in unknown problems for future generations.

daydream EDUCATION

Understanding Genetics & Evolution

Evidence For Evolution by Natural Selection

The theory of evolution by natural selection is now widely accepted because of evidence that it has happened in the past and is still happening today.

The fossil record shows a sequence of progressive changes in body form, leading from ancient ancestors to modern species.

The theory of genetics has shown how characteristics can be inherited from one generation to the next, in the form of genes.

There are examples of natural selection occurring today – for example, the evolution of antibiotic resistance in bacteria.

Fossils

Fossils are the remains of organisms from millions of years ago, found in rocks.

Fossil Formation

- Organisms or parts of them may be preserved when the conditions needed for decay are absent (e.g. insects preserved in amber).

- The hard parts of organisms may be replaced by minerals as they decay, leaving an impression in the rock formed around them.

- Traces of organisms such as footprints, burrows and rootlet traces may be preserved when the mud they were formed in turns to rock.

Fossilisation usually preserves only the hard parts of an organism. Therefore, there are few traces of the earliest forms of life, which were mainly soft-bodied organisms.

Whatever traces may have existed have been destroyed by geological activity. As a result, scientists cannot be certain how and when life first evolved. The whole fossil record is very incomplete because the conditions for fossilisation rarely occur.

Extinction

Extinction occurs when there are no remaining individuals of a species left alive. Extinction can occur for a variety of reasons:

- The climate may change, and the species cannot adapt to the new climate quickly enough.
- The species' habitat may be destroyed, leaving it nowhere to live.
- Another similar species may arrive and out-compete the existing species.
- A predator may wipe out the entire population. Humans are the most common cause of this.

Resistant Bacteria

Evolution is a process that occurs gradually over many generations. As a result, until recently, it has only been possible to find evidence of evolution through fossils.

However, some simple organisms, such as bacteria, reproduce at a rapid rate, so they evolve quickly. This enables scientists to monitor how such organisms evolve through natural selection.

Some bacteria, such as the MRSA bacterium, have evolved a resistance to most antibiotics.

Natural Selection in Antibiotic-Resistant Bacteria

1 Resistant strains of bacteria are not killed when infections are treated with antibiotics.

2 Whilst non-resistant strains die, the resistant strains survive, reproduce and increase in numbers.

3 The resistant strain spreads because people are not immune to it and antibiotics are unable to treat it.

The overuse and misuse of antibiotics has led to an increase in antibiotic-resistant bacteria.

Slowing the Development Rate of Resistant Bacteria

- Overuse of antibiotics causes bacteria to mutate, so doctors are encouraged not to prescribe antibiotics for viral or non-serious infections.
- Failing to complete a full course of antibiotics can result in bacteria surviving and mutating into resistant forms. Therefore, patients must complete their full course of antibiotics.
- Overuse of antibiotics in agriculture (e.g. dosing cattle with antibiotics to prevent infection) should be restricted.

These measures are very important because new forms of antibiotics cannot be developed as quickly as new resistant strains of bacteria emerge. This may mean that some infections can no longer be controlled.

Classification of Living Organisms

Linnaeus's Classification Model

Traditionally, living things have been classified into groups depending on their characteristics. The Linnaeus system divides living organisms into five kingdoms, which are then subdivided into smaller and smaller groups.

Each species is given a scientific name, which consists of two words. The first indicates the genus, the second the species. This is known as the binomial system.

Tiger (*Panthera tigris*)

French rose (*Rosa gallica*)

Decrease in similarity / Increase in numbers

Increase in similarity / Decrease in numbers

	Tiger	French rose
Kingdom	Animalia	Plantae
Phylum	Chordata	Angiospermae
Class	Mammalia	Dicotyledoneae
Order	Carnivora	Rosales
Family	Felidae	Rosaceae
Genus	Panthera	Rosa
Species	*Panthera tigris*	*Rosa gallica*

Members of the same species can appear to be very different from each other. If they are the same species, they can breed together to produce fertile offspring.

Three-Domain System

Improvements in microscopes and the understanding of biochemical processes have meant that classification systems have had to be updated. Based on evidence from the chemical analysis of genetic material, a new three-domain system was proposed by Carl Woese in 1977.

In this system, organisms are divided into:

Bacteria
Cells with no nucleus; true bacteria

Archaea
Cells with no nucleus; primitive bacteria often found in extreme environments

Eukaryota
Cells with a nucleus; includes protists, fungi, plants and animals

These are then subdivided into the smaller groups used in the five-kingdom system.

Evolutionary Trees

Evolutionary trees are used by scientists to show how they believe organisms are related.

To show common ancestors and relationships between species, scientists use current classification data for living organisms and fossil data for extinct organisms.

The further up the evolutionary tree an organism is, the more recently it branched from the other species on the tree from a common ancestor. Species that are closer on the tree are more closely related.

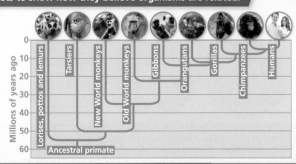

Millions of years ago: 0, 10, 20, 30, 40, 50, 60

Lorises, pottos and lemurs · Tarsiers · New World monkeys · Old World monkeys · Gibbons · Orangutans · Gorillas · Chimpanzees · Humans

Ancestral primate

Evolutionary trees are also known as phylogenetic trees.

Adaptations, Interdependence & Competition

Communities

An ecosystem is a community of living organisms together with their physical environment. It includes the interactions between the living (**biotic**) and non-living (**abiotic**) components.

Key Terms		
Habitat	The place where organisms live	
Community	All the living things in an ecosystem	
Population	All the organisms of any one species living in a habitat	
Organism	An individual living thing	

Competition and Interdependence

In ecosystems, living things interact with each other and their habitat in different ways. **Interspecific competition** is competition between organisms of different species, whereas **intraspecific competition** is competition between organisms of the same species.

Organisms compete for resources from their surroundings and from other living organisms, but they also depend on each other to survive and reproduce.

Within a community, plants compete for light, space, water and minerals, whereas animals compete for food, water, territory and mates.

	Tomato Plant	Bee	Thrush
Organism			
Competes with	*Other plants for light, water and minerals.*	*Other bees and some other insects for food*	*Other birds for food and nesting sites*
Depends on	*Insects for pollination; animals to distribute seeds (by eating fruit)*	*Plants for food (nectar)*	*Invertebrates for food; plants for nesting sites*

Interdependence

All parts of an ecosystem are interdependent. This means that if one factor changes, it will affect the other parts of the ecosystem.

The weather is hot and little rainfall occurs. → Fewer plants grow. → Less food & shelter cause grasshopper and mouse populations to shrink. → Less food causes rat and snake populations to shrink. → Less food causes the owl population to shrink.

The more interactions there are within a community, the greater the level of interdependence. A high level of interdependence often leads to a stable community where all the biotic and abiotic factors are in balance. As a result, the population sizes remain fairly constant. In small communities, the removal of a single species can have major effects.

daydream
EDUCATION

There are various factors within an environment that can affect the function of ecosystems. These factors are categorised as abiotic or biotic.

Abiotic Factors

An abiotic factor in an ecosystem is one that is non-living. These include:

light intensity   temperature   moisture levels   oxygen levels

carbon dioxide levels   wind intensity and direction   soil pH and mineral content

The importance of these factors varies in different ecosystems and for different organisms. Light intensity, soil type and carbon dioxide levels are usually only significant for plants, whereas oxygen levels are most important for aquatic animals that need oxygen dissolved in the water for aerobic respiration.

The example in the Interdependence section shows how an abiotic factor (lack of rainfall) can affect the whole community within an ecosystem.

Biotic Factors

A biotic factor in an ecosystem is one that is living. These include:

| Introduction of predators | Availability of food | Competing species | Introduction of diseases (pathogens) |

These biotic factors can have devastating effects on a community, causing imbalances in organism populations and an unstable community.

Each factor has direct and indirect effects on a community. For example, the introduction of a new predator into a community will not only lead to a decrease in the prey population, but it will also indirectly affect other organisms in the community that are dependent on the prey.

Adaptation

Organisms have features (adaptations) that help them to survive in their natural habitat.

Structural	Behavioural	Functional
Physical features that help organisms to survive	*Learned or inborn behaviours that help organisms to survive*	*Bodily processes that help organisms to survive*
Cacti have spines instead of leaves to reduce water loss by evaporation and transpiration, and to protect them from predators.	*Polar bears dig deep dens in the snow to protect themselves from strong winds.*	*Snakes and spiders produce poisonous venom, which helps with protection and immobilising prey.*

Some organisms, known as extremophiles, are highly specialised so that they can live in extreme conditions, such as high temperatures (thermophiles) or high salt concentrations (halophiles).

Organisation of an Ecosystem

All living organisms need a supply of nutrients to survive and build biomass.

Photosynthetic organisms (mainly green plants and algae) can produce their own food using light energy and inorganic materials through photosynthesis. They are called **producers**. They use this food to provide energy for other life processes.

All other organisms obtain energy from eating other organisms. They are called **consumers**. The original source of all the energy in living organisms is the Sun.

Food Chains

The feeding relationships in a community can be represented in the form of food chains, which show the direct transfer of energy between organisms in an ecosystem.

| The Sun is the source of all energy. | Producers use light energy to synthesise molecules for energy and growth. | Primary consumers feed on producers. | Secondary consumers feed on producers and primary consumers. | Tertiary consumers can feed on all other consumers. |

Predator and Prey Relationships

Consumers that eat other animals are predators, and those that are eaten are prey. In stable communities, the numbers of predators and prey rise and fall in cycles.

An increase in prey will support a larger number of predators. However, when the predators increase, they will eat more prey, reducing their numbers.

When the prey population is reduced, the population will be able to support fewer predators. This occurs in a continuous cycle.

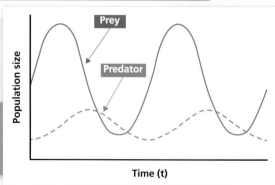

Prey

Predator

Population size

Time (t)

daydream
EDUCATION

Measuring the Abundance and Distribution of Organisms

It is not always possible to collect information on a whole population. In such instances, a proportion (sample) of the population is used instead. Ecologists use a wide range of sampling methods to determine the abundance and distribution of species in an ecosystem.

Quadrats

A quadrat is a square frame of a specific size (often 0.5 × 0.5 m). It is used to sample an area that is too big to completely survey.

The number of one or more species in each quadrat is counted and then scaled up to estimate the number in the whole area.

Rules for Using Quadrats

| The positioning of the quadrats must be random to avoid bias. | The number of quadrats must be sufficient to give a representative picture of the whole area. | Diverse habitats need a larger number of quadrats than uniform habitats. |

Quadrat Example: Estimate the total number of snails in a habitat that is 4,000 m².

Total area of habitat = 4,000 m²

Number of quadrats used = 100

Area of 1 quadrat = 0.25 m²

Total area sampled = 0.25 × 100 = 25 m²

Number of snails in sample area (100 quadrats or 25 m²) = 80

Total number of snails in whole habitat = $\frac{4,000}{25}$ × 80 = 12,800

Transects

A transect is a line, usually marked by a rope or tape measure, that is used to measure the distribution of organisms, not their numbers.

Samples are taken at regular intervals along the line, and the species seen at each point are recorded. The line is usually laid along some sort of gradient to see its effect on distribution (e.g. low tide mark to high tide mark).

Mathematical Terms Used in Ecology

When collecting data on the abundance of organisms in an ecosystem, you will often need to calculate averages, or the middle value of a data set. There are three main types of averages.

Mean	Median	Mode
The sum of all values divided by the number of values	The middle value when data is arranged in order of size (If there is an even number of values, it is the mean of the two middle numbers.)	The value that occurs most often

Cycling Materials

The materials that living things need to survive and reproduce are in limited supply. Therefore, they must be constantly recycled for life to persist.

The Carbon Cycle

All life on earth is carbon based. Therefore, a constant supply of carbon is needed to support life. Carbon is cycled mainly through the processes of respiration and photosynthesis, but also through combustion and decay.

Respiration, combustion and decay release carbon dioxide into the atmosphere, whereas photosynthesis removes it from the atmosphere.

Key Terms

Combustion

Energy and carbon dioxide are released when fossil fuels are burned.

Photosynthesis

Sunlight is used to convert carbon dioxide and water into glucose (which contains carbon) and oxygen.

Respiration

Glucose and oxygen are converted into energy, carbon dioxide and water.

Decay

Organic matter decomposes, releasing carbon dioxide, methane, energy, water and minerals.

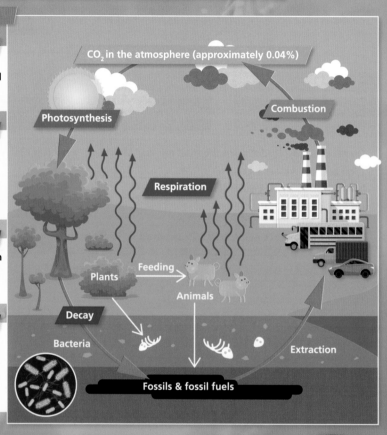

CO$_2$ in the atmosphere (approximately 0.04%)

Photosynthesis

Combustion

Respiration

Plants

Feeding

Animals

Decay

Bacteria

Extraction

Fossils & fossil fuels

Microorganisms in the Carbon Cycle

Microorganisms play a vital role in the carbon cycle (and other cycles). They decay the remains of plants and animals and return the carbon in them to the atmosphere by respiration.

Decay also releases important mineral ions back into the soil.

daydream
EDUCATION

The Water Cycle

All living organisms need water. Therefore, a constant supply of water is needed to support life.

Water is the only chemical compound that occurs naturally on Earth's surface in all three physical states: solid, liquid and gas.

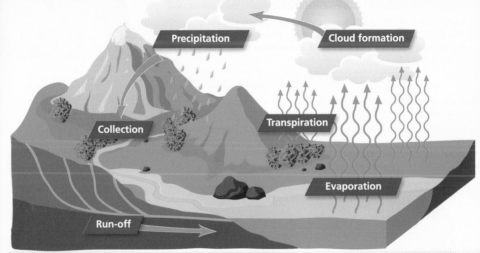

Precipitation

Cloud formation

Collection

Transpiration

Evaporation

Run-off

1 Water in oceans, rivers and lakes evaporates and, as it is heated, turns into water vapour.

2 Water also evaporates from the leaves of green plants by transpiration.

3 As the water vapour rises, it cools and condenses into clouds.

4 The water in clouds eventually falls as precipitation (rain, sleet, snow).

5 The water provides fresh water for plants and animals on land.

6 Water runs back into the sea at different rates through surface flow and groundwater flow.

The Nitrogen Cycle

Nitrogen makes up almost 80% of the atmosphere and is found in all proteins and DNA. Like water and carbon, it is recycled to provide the building blocks for future organisms.

Because nitrogen is so unreactive, it cannot be used directly by plants and animals. Therefore, it must be converted into other chemical forms before it is usable.

Bacteria and other single-celled prokaryotes convert nitrogen into usable forms in a process called nitrogen fixation. This releases nitrates into the soil which are then absorbed by plants. Animals obtain nitrogen by eating plants and other animals.

Biodiversity

Biodiversity is the variety of species in a given area. There are two aspects to biodiversity: the number of different species present and the number of individuals of each species.

Biodiversity makes ecosystems more stable. The more species there are, the less dependent each species is on another for food or shelter because there are always alternatives.

The future of humans relies on us maintaining a good level of biodiversity on the planet, yet many human activities are reducing it. As a result, many measures are now being taken to maintain biodiversity.

Waste Management

Waste causes different types of pollution, which damage ecosystems and seriously reduce biodiversity.

Increased life expectancies due to improved health care and medicine have caused the human population to grow. This, combined with an increase in people's standard of living, has meant that more resources are being used and more waste is being created.

Water Pollution

Water pollution can cause significant damage to marine ecosystems. Toxic chemicals, sewage and fertilisers from industry and agriculture all contribute to water pollution.

Air Pollution

Air pollution damages human health and can destroy whole ecosystems. The burning of fossil fuels for energy has increased the amount of greenhouse gases and chemicals in the atmosphere.

Land Pollution

Land pollution can damage ecosystems and contaminate water supplies. The disposal of waste in landfill sites and the use of toxic chemicals in farming are two of the main causes of land pollution.

Land Use

As the human population grows, more land is used for building, farming, quarrying and dumping waste. This destroys habitats and reduces the amount of land available for animals and plants.

Peat bogs are specialised habitats, and the species that live there are adapted to that environment. Peat is used for garden compost and as a fuel.

The removal of peat destroys the habitat of animals and plants, and burning it releases greenhouse gases such as carbon dioxide into the atmosphere.

daydream EDUCATION

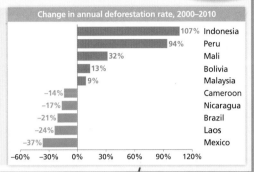

Rate of Deforestation

Deforestation is the clearing of rainforests and wooded areas. It is estimated that 50% of the world's tropical rainforests have been lost to deforestation over the last 100 years.

Increased awareness of the importance of tropical rainforests has led many countries, such as Brazil, to reduce their deforestation rates.

Although the global rate is decreasing, it continues to increase in some areas. For example, in Indonesia, large areas of the rainforest are being cleared to make way for palm oil plantations. Indonesia is the world's biggest producer of palm oil, and its economy relies on its production.

Change in annual deforestation rate, 2000–2010

Indonesia	107%
Peru	94%
Mali	32%
Bolivia	13%
Malaysia	9%
Cameroon	−14%
Nicaragua	−17%
Brazil	−21%
Laos	−24%
Mexico	−37%

Causes of Deforestation

There are many reasons why rainforests are being destroyed.

Overpopulation
As population grows, trees are cleared to make room for settlements.

Mining
Trees and vegetation are cleared so that valuable metals and minerals can be mined.

Logging
Trees are felled to harvest timber for profit. Roads must also be built to access logging sites, requiring further deforestation.

Farming & Agriculture
Trees are cleared to create space for crops and grazing livestock.

Energy Development
Forests are flooded to build dams for hydroelectric power (HEP), and areas are razed to make way for biofuel crops.

Impacts of Deforestation

Indigenous peoples have long cleared small areas of forest with little damage. However, modern, large-scale deforestation has had huge environmental, economic and social impacts.

Trees remove CO_2 from the atmosphere. Therefore, deforestation leads to increased CO_2 levels, which contribute to the greenhouse effect and rising global temperatures. Fewer trees means fewer roots to soak up water from the soil, so more nutrients are leached. Deforestation also reduces biodiversity: plants and animals become extinct due to a lack of food and shelter.

In 1500, 6.9 million people were living in the Amazon rainforest. With homes having been destroyed by deforestation, only 200,000 remain there. Moreover, deforestation's effects make these areas less attractive to tourists, leading to lost income. However, more jobs are being created through logging, farming and mining. Also, selling timber can be very profitable.

Global Warming: Causes & Effects

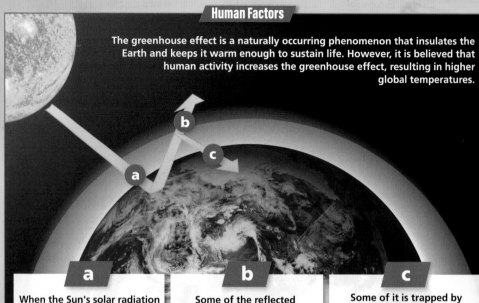

Human Factors

The greenhouse effect is a naturally occurring phenomenon that insulates the Earth and keeps it warm enough to sustain life. However, it is believed that human activity increases the greenhouse effect, resulting in higher global temperatures.

a
When the Sun's solar radiation reaches the Earth's surface, most of it is absorbed, but some is reflected into the atmosphere.

b
Some of the reflected solar energy passes through the atmosphere and back into space.

c
Some of it is trapped by greenhouse gases in the atmosphere, such as methane and CO_2, increasing the temperature of the Earth.

Several human activities increase the levels of greenhouse gases in the atmosphere, trapping more of the Sun's solar energy.

This graph shows the correlation between the average global temperature and the level of CO_2 in the atmosphere over time.

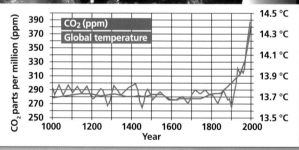

CO₂ parts per million (ppm)

| CO2 (ppm) |
| Global temperature |

390 — 14.5 °C
370 — 14.3 °C
350 — 14.1 °C
330 — 13.9 °C
310 —
290 — 13.7 °C
270 —
250 — 13.5 °C

1000   1200   1400   1600   1800   2000

Year

daydream
EDUCATION

Fossil Fuels

Fossil fuels such as oil, gas and coal are burnt to generate energy for transportation, manufacturing and electricity production.

However, the process of burning fossil fuels releases CO_2 into the atmosphere and is the main source of greenhouse gas emissions.

Agriculture

Agriculture, especially livestock and rice farming, produces huge amounts of the greenhouse gas methane.

It is released by animals during digestion and by matter decomposed by microbes in flooded rice paddy fields.

Deforestation

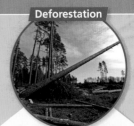

Trees remove CO_2 from the atmosphere for photosynthesis. Therefore, clearing trees results in less CO_2 being removed from the atmosphere.

This is worsened by the burning of fossil fuels, which also releases greenhouse gases into the atmosphere.

Effects of Climate Change

Climate change has a significant effect on both the environment and people.

Effects on the Environment

Warmer global temperatures will cause glaciers and ice sheets to melt, leading to rising sea levels and the loss of polar habitats.

Rising sea levels will result in low-lying coastal areas flooding more frequently or even becoming permanently submerged in water.

Many species of plants and animals are at risk of becoming extinct as their habitats are altered or damaged by climate change. For example, many of the world's coral reefs, which support a diverse range of marine life, are at risk of bleaching and destruction due to rising sea temperatures.

Warmer temperatures and higher sea levels will lead to more extreme weather events and a change in precipitation patterns.

Effects on People

As global temperatures rise, people in already hot regions will be at increased risk of developing heat-related health problems.

Many coastal areas at risk of flooding and areas that experience extremely high temperatures may become uninhabitable. This could lead to mass migration and overcrowding in areas less at risk.

Although agriculture in some areas may benefit from warmer temperatures, many areas will become hotter and drier. This will result in drought, desertification and declining crop yields.

Drought and reduced crop yields will cause food and water shortages in many areas.

Maintaining Biodiversity

To preserve biodiversity, it is important to ensure the negative impacts of human interactions with ecosystems are kept to a minimum.

As the negative impacts of human interactions with ecosystems have become clearer, measures have been taken by scientists and concerned citizens to change these interactions and reduce their impacts on biodiversity.

Breeding Programmes

Breeding programmes for endangered species have been set up in zoos and wildlife parks. These aim to breed the animals in protected conditions and then release them back into the wild.

Protection & Regeneration

Rare and endangered habitats in nature reserves and national parks, for example, are protected by laws and regulations. Also, some habitats are being regenerated by careful management.

Reintroducing Hedgerows

Where farmers grow large areas of one type of crop (known as monoculture), hedgerows provide a haven of biodiversity. Many were removed in the past to make it easier to use large farm machinery, but they are now being reintroduced, sometimes with government grants.

Reducing CO_2 Emissions

Some governments are taking steps to reduce deforestation and CO_2 emissions. Many South American countries have laws that limit deforestation to preserve the Amazon rainforest. Many governments are also setting targets for lower CO_2 emissions.

Recycling

Efforts are being made to encourage people to recycle and reuse resources where possible to reduce the amount of waste being dumped in landfill sites.

Conflicting Pressures of Maintaining Biodiversity

Many of the measures aimed at maintaining biodiversity can conflict with the economic needs of a population. This is especially true in developing countries where ongoing economic development is vital for food, water and energy security.

For example, by implementing laws to prevent the deforestation of land that could be used for agriculture, mining and energy development, many countries risk damaging the economy and the livelihoods of local people.

daydream EDUCATION

Chemistry

The Atom

All substances are made of atoms. An atom is the smallest part of an element that can exist.

Development of Atomic Theory

The model of the atom has changed over time as new experimental evidence has been discovered.

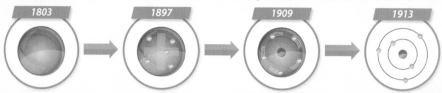

1803 — 1897 — 1909 — 1913

Dalton's Model
Atoms were believed to be tiny spheres that could not be divided.

Thomson's Model
After the discovery of electrons, it was proposed that atoms were balls of positive charge with embedded negative electrons. This model is known as the plum pudding model.

Rutherford's Model
Alpha particle scattering experiments found that the mass of the atom was concentrated at its centre in a positively charged nucleus.

Bohr's Model
Calculations showed that electrons orbit the nucleus in shells that are fixed distances from the nucleus.

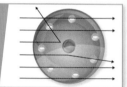

In Rutherford's experiments, alpha particles were fired at a thin piece of gold foil. Rather than pass through the foil as expected, some particles were deflected, and some bounced back.

This meant that the plum pudding model could not be correct, so Rutherford proposed that there must be a positively charged nucleus at the centre of the atom. This model is known as the nuclear model.

After Bohr's theory of atomic structure was accepted, further experiments by Rutherford showed evidence of smaller positively charged particles (protons) within the nucleus.

This was then developed further, with James Chadwick providing evidence to show the existence of neutral particles (neutrons) within the nucleus.

Particle Name	Relative Charge	Mass
Proton	+1	1
Neutron	0	1
Electron	−1	Very small

Electron Structure of Carbon: 2,4

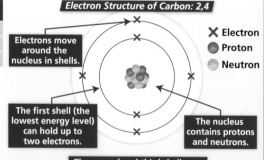

Electrons move around the nucleus in shells.

The first shell (the lowest energy level) can hold up to two electrons.

The second and third shells can hold up to eight electrons.

The nucleus contains protons and neutrons.

✗ Electron
● Proton
○ Neutron

Atoms have no overall electrical charge because they contain an equal number of protons and electrons. Almost all (99.9%) of an atom's mass is in the nucleus.

Atoms are very small, with a radius of about 0.1 nm (1×10^{-10} m). The radius of a nucleus is less than 1/10,000 of that of the atom (about 1×10^{-14} m).

If an atom were blown up to the size of a football stadium, the nucleus would be the size of a small pea on the centre circle. The electrons would be orbiting around the outermost edge, but they would be far too small to be seen.

daydream EDUCATION

Atoms and Elements

The number of protons, electrons and neutrons in atoms varies. However, it is the number of protons in the nucleus of an atom that determines what type of atom it is.

Atom	Number of Protons
Helium	2
Oxygen	8
Aluminium	13

An element is a substance that contains only one type of atom and therefore cannot be broken down into simpler components by any non-nuclear chemical reaction.

Atomic Number & Mass Number

Mass Number

The sum of protons and neutrons in an atom

Atomic Number

This is the number of protons (and electrons) in an atom.

Element Symbol

Elements have a one or two-letter chemical symbol. For example, C is the chemical symbol for carbon.

Isotopes

Although atoms of an element will always have the same number of protons (and atomic number), they can have a different number of neutrons and, therefore, a different mass number. These are called isotopes.

Calculating Relative Atomic Mass

The relative atomic mass of an element is shown on the periodic table. Sometimes, this is not a whole number. That is because it is an average based on the abundance of each isotope that exists.

Example 1

35.5
Cl
Chlorine
17

25% of chlorine isotopes have a mass of 37.
75% of chlorine isotopes have a mass of 35.

All figures are rounded to the nearest whole number.

Relative atomic mass $(A_r) = \dfrac{(25 \times 37) + (75 \times 35)}{100} = 35.5$

Example 2

24.3
Mg
Magnesium
12

79% of magnesium isotopes have a mass of 24.
10% of magnesium isotopes have a mass of 25.
11% of magnesium isotopes have a mass of 26.

All figures are rounded to the nearest whole number.

Relative atomic mass $(A_r) = \dfrac{(24 \times 79) + (25 \times 10) + (26 \times 11)}{100} = 24.3$

Compounds

Compounds contain two or more elements that are chemically combined.

Chemical reactions can be represented by word equations or equations using symbols and formulae.

Compounds are formed during chemical reactions.

Chemical reactions always involve the formation of one or more new substances and often involve an energy change.

The elements in the compounds are in fixed proportions and are held together by chemical bonds. Compounds can be separated back into elements only by chemical reactions.

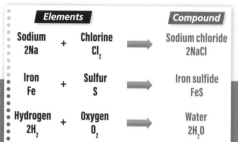

Elements			Compound
Sodium $2Na$	+	Chlorine Cl_2	Sodium chloride $2NaCl$
Iron Fe	+	Sulfur S	Iron sulfide FeS
Hydrogen $2H_2$	+	Oxygen O_2	Water $2H_2O$

To form compounds, bonds are formed. To do this, elements gain, lose or share electrons.

Ionic Bonding

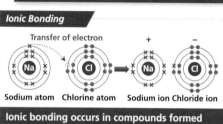

Transfer of electron

Sodium atom   Chlorine atom   Sodium ion   Chloride ion

Ionic bonding occurs in compounds formed when metal atoms react with non-metal atoms.

Electrons are transferred from the outer shell of the metal to the outer shell of the non-metal. The metal atoms lose electrons to form positive ions, and the non-metal atoms gain electrons to form negative ions.

Covalent Bonding

Hydrogen atom   Chlorine atom   Hydrogen chloride (HCl)

Covalent bonding occurs in most non-metallic elements and in compounds of non-metals.

In covalent bonding, pairs of electrons are shared to form molecules. The types and number of atoms in a molecule are shown in its formula.

Naming Compounds

Some basic rules apply to naming compounds.

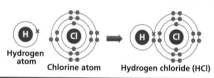

Oxygen + Magnesium = Magnesium oxide

The metal is written first. | The non-metal comes last. Oxygen forms oxide ions.

Non-Metal Ions

The suffix -ide shows that there is only one non-metal element in the compound.

Chlorine ⟹ Chloride (Cl^-)   Bromine ⟹ Bromide (Br^-)

Sulfur ⟹ Sulfide (S^{2-})

Non-metal ions can contain more than one element. The suffix -ate shows that the compound contains oxygen.

Carbonate (CO_3^{2-}) | Sulfate (SO_4^{2-}) | Nitrate (NO_3^-)

daydream
EDUCATION

Chemical Equations

A chemical equation is a written representation of the process that occurs in a chemical reaction.

The white sparks from a sparkler are created when magnesium burns. Magnesium reacts with oxygen in the air to form magnesium oxide.

The word equation for this reaction is:

Magnesium + Oxygen ➡ Magnesium oxide

Word equations are a simple way of displaying a chemical reaction. However, they do not show the number of atoms involved.

Symbol Equations

During a chemical reaction, no atoms are lost or made. Therefore, the total number of atoms on each side of a chemical equation must be the same. Symbol equations show the number of atoms involved in a chemical reaction.

Reactants $2Mg$ + O_2 ➡ $2MgO$ **Products**

This can also be shown as a particle diagram.

The number of oxygen and magnesium atoms is the same on both sides. The symbol equation is balanced.

State Symbols

To complete a balanced symbol equation, you can also add state symbols to show the state of each substance.

$$2Mg\,(s) + O_2\,(g) \longrightarrow 2MgO\,(s)$$

State symbols   (s) solid   (g) gas   (l) liquid   (aq) aqueous (a solution in water)

Sometimes chemical formulae contain brackets. These are used when a compound contains a chemical group. For example, the chemical formula for magnesium hydroxide is $Mg(OH)_2$.

OH is a hydroxide group, and magnesium hydroxide has two of them. Therefore, the compound contains one atom of magnesium, two of oxygen and two of hydrogen.

Numbers in Chemical Equations

The chemical formula for sulfuric acid is shown below.

This number indicates the number of atoms or molecules of a substance in the reaction. It can be changed to balance an equation.

$$2H_2SO_4$$

These numbers indicate how many atoms of an element are in a compound. These numbers cannot be changed to balance an equation.

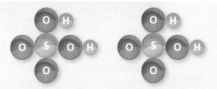

The formula shows that there are two molecules of sulfuric acid, and each one contains two hydrogen atoms, one sulfur atom and four oxygen atoms.

Brackets in Chemical Equations

Sometimes, brackets are used in a formula to indicate a chemical group.

This is the formula for calcium hydroxide.

$$Ca(OH)_2$$

One atom of calcium has two hydroxide groups (–OH) attached to it. The compound contains one atom of calcium, two of oxygen and two of hydrogen. The number below the bracket cannot be changed to balance the equation.

Writing Chemical Equations

1 Write the word equation.

Hydrogen + Chlorine ⟶ Hydrogen chloride

2 Write the symbols for each substance, including state symbols.

$H_2 (g) + Cl_2 (g) \longrightarrow HCl (g)$

3 Count the number of atoms of each element on both sides of the equation to determine if it is balanced.

Reactants ($H_2 + Cl_2$)		Products (HCl)	
Element	Atoms	Element	Atoms
H	2	H	1
Cl	2	Cl	1

This is not balanced. There are fewer atoms in the product.

4 If the equation is not balanced, work out how many more atoms are needed.

You need to double the number of hydrogen and chlorine atoms in the product to balance the equation.

5 Write the balanced symbol equation.

$H_2 (g) + Cl_2 (g) \longrightarrow 2HCl (g)$

Remember: You can only change the numbers in front of symbols. You cannot change the small subscript numbers.

HCl ⟹ 2HCl ✓   HCl ⟹ H_2Cl_2 ✗

Examples

Group 1 Metal and Water	Sodium $2Na (s)$	+	Water $2H_2O (l)$	Sodium hydroxide $2NaOH (aq)$	+	Hydrogen $H_2 (g)$
Acid and Alkali (Neutralisation)	Hydrochloric acid $HCl (aq)$	+	Potassium hydroxide $KOH (aq)$	Potassium chloride $KCl (aq)$	+	Water $H_2O (l)$
Combustion (Burning) of Methane	Methane $CH_4 (g)$	+	Oxygen $2O_2 (g)$	Carbon dioxide $CO_2 (g)$	+	Water $2H_2O (l)$

Periodic Table

The periodic table is all of the known elements in order of atomic number. Atoms of each element are represented by a chemical symbol.

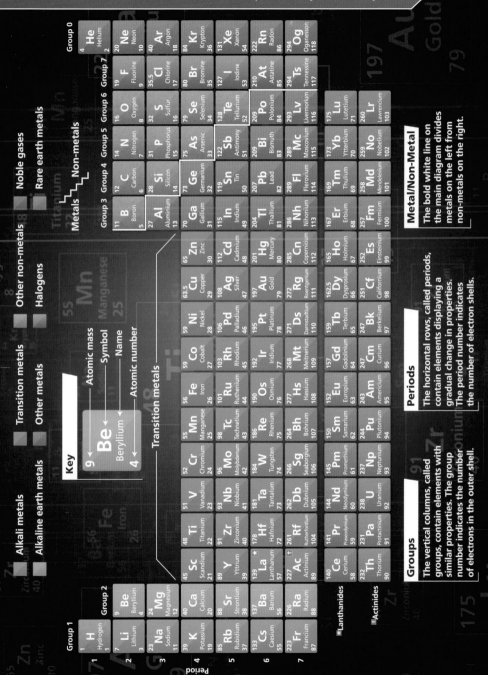

Key

9 — Atomic mass
Be — Symbol
Beryllium — Name
4 — Atomic number

Groups

The vertical columns, called groups, contain elements with similar properties. The group number indicates the number of electrons in the outer shell.

Periods

The horizontal rows, called periods, contain elements displaying a gradual change in properties. The period number indicates the number of electron shells.

Metal/Non-Metal

The bold white line on the main diagram divides metals on the left from non-metals on the right.

Alkali metals
Alkaline earth metals
Transition metals
Other metals
Other non-metals
Halogens
Noble gases
Rare earth metals
Metals
Non-metals

Development of the Periodic Table

Before the discovery of atomic structure, scientists attempted to classify the elements by arranging them in order of their atomic weights. However, many early tables were incomplete, and some elements were placed in unsuitable groups.

Mendeleev's Periodic Table

Today's periodic table is based on one devised by the Russian scientist Dmitri Mendeleev in 1869. Mendeleev ordered the elements according to atomic weights. However, he realised that there may be other undiscovered elements and so left gaps in his table. He also adjusted the order in consideration of the chemical properties of elements.

When he ordered the elements based on their chemical properties, they ended up in order of their atomic numbers. Mendeleev did not recognise this because protons had not been discovered yet.

Series	Group I	Group II	Group III	Group IV	Group V	Group VI	Group VII	Group VIII
1	H=1	-	-	-	-	-	-	-
2	Li=7	Be=9.4	B=11	C=12	N=14	O=16	F=19	-
3	Na=23	Mg=24	Al=27.3	Si=28	P=31	S=32	Cl=35.5	-
4	K=39	Ca=40	-=44	Ti=48	V=51	Cr=52	Mn=55	Fe=56, Co=59, Ni=59, Cu=63
5	(Cu)=63	Zn=65	-=68	-=72	As=75	Se=78	Br=80	-
6	Rb=85	Sr=87	?Yt=88	Zr=90	Nb=94	Mo=96	-=100	Ru=104, Rh=104, Pd=106, Ag=108
7	(Ag)=108	Cd=112	In=113	Sn=118	Sb=122	Te=125	J=127	-
8	Cs=133	Ba=137	?Di=138	?Ce=140	-	-	-	-
9	(-)	-	-	-	-	-	-	-
10	-	-	?Er=178	?La=180	Ta=182	W=184	-	Os=195, Ir=197, Pt=198, Au=199
11	(Au)=199	Hg=200	Tl=204	Pb=207	Bi=208	-	-	-
12	-	-	-	Th=231	-	U=240	-	-

Later Modifications

Soon after Mendeleev published his table, new elements that had properties that matched the gaps in his table (e.g. gallium, scandium and germanium) were discovered.

Since the discovery of protons, the periodic table has been structured in order of atomic number rather than atomic weight. This is more accurate than atomic weight, which varies in different isotopes, because it is constant.

daydream EDUCATION

Metals and Non-Metals

Metals and Non-Metals

When atoms react, they either lose, gain or share electrons to form a full outer shell of electrons. Atoms that lose electrons form positive ions, and atoms that gain electrons form negative ions.

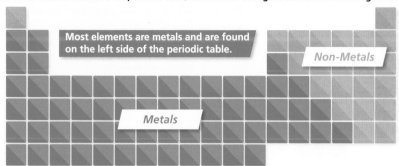

Most elements are metals and are found on the left side of the periodic table.

Non-Metals

Metals

Metals

Elements that react to form positive ions are metals. Metals have fewer electrons on their outer shell so are more likely to lose electrons and form positive ions.

Non-Metals

Elements that react to form negative ions are non-metals. Non-metals have more electrons on their outer shell so are more likely to gain electrons and form negative ions.

Non-metals that form negative ions can react with metals to form ionic compounds. Metals cannot react with other metals because positive ions repel each other.

Non-metals that do not form ions can share electrons with each other to form molecules with covalent bonds.

Properties of Metals and Non-Metals

Metals	Non-Metals
Good conductors of heat and electricity	Poor conductors of heat and electricity (except graphite, which conducts electricity)
High density	Low density
Malleable (can be hammered into shape)	Brittle (when solid)
Ductile (can be stretched into wires)	Non-ductile
High melting and boiling points (except mercury)	Low melting and boiling points
React with non-metals to form positive ions in ionic compounds	React with metals to form negative ions in ionic compounds
Do not react with other metals	React with other non-metals to form molecules
Form basic oxides	Form acidic oxides

Groups in the Periodic Table

Group 1 elements are known as alkali metals. They have only one electron in their outer shell. Therefore, they are very reactive and readily form ionic compounds.

As you move down the column, the elements become more reactive. This is because the outer electron is further away from the nucleus, which means there is a weaker force of attraction between them. Therefore, melting and boiling points decrease as you move down the group.

Increasing reactivity

7	Li	Lithium	3
23	Na	Sodium	11
39	K	Potassium	19
85	Rb	Rubidium	37
133	Cs	Caesium	55
223	Fr	Francium	87

Lithium

Potassium

Physical Properties

- Low densities*
- Low melting points*
- Form compounds that are soluble white solids

*compared to other metals

- Form positive ions with a single positive charge
- Soft and malleable
- Conduct electricity

Francium does not share these properties. It is highly unstable and breaks down as soon as it is formed.

Metal	Reaction with Water	Reaction with Chlorine	Reaction with Oxygen
All	Metal + Water = Metal hydroxide + Hydrogen	Metal + Chlorine = Metal chloride	Metal + Oxygen = Metal oxide
Lithium	Bubbles, fizzes, moves on the surface of the water and becomes smaller until it disappears	Forms lithium chloride, a white powder	Forms lithium oxide; burns with a red flame
Sodium	Bubbles, fizzes, moves on the surface of the water and melts. The hydrogen may burn with an orange flame	Reacts more vigorously than with water; produces sodium chloride, a white powder	Forms sodium oxide; burns with a yellow flame
Potassium	Bubbles, fizzes, moves on the surface of the water and melts. The hydrogen ignites, sometimes causing an explosion	Reacts violently with the chlorine to produce potassium chloride	Forms potassium oxide; burns with a lilac flame

Alkali metals are often stored in oil to stop them from reacting with oxygen and water vapour in the air.

daydream
EDUCATION

The periodic table organises elements in order of increasing atomic number. Elements in the same vertical column have the same number of electrons in their outer shell and therefore have similar chemical properties.

Group 0 — Noble Gases

4
He
Helium
2

20
Ne
Neon
10

40
Ar
Argon
18

84
Kr
Krypton
36

131
Xe
Xenon
54

222
Rn
Radon
86

Group 0 elements have a full outer shell of electrons. Therefore, they do not need to gain or lose electrons to become more stable, and they are inert (very unreactive).

Noble gases exist as single atoms that are not bonded together, and their boiling points increase as you move down the column. This is because as molecules get bigger, the intermolecular forces between the atoms increase.

Physical Properties

- Colourless gases
- Very low melting points
- Non-metals
- Poor conductors
- Non-flammable
- Very unreactive

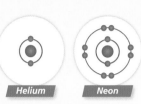

Helium   *Neon*

All elements in this group have eight electrons in their outer shell, except for helium, which has two.

Group 7 — Halogens

Decreasing reactivity

19
F
Fluorine
9

35.5
Cl
Chlorine
17

80
Br
Bromine
35

127
I
Iodine
53

210
At
Astatine
85

Group 7 elements are non-metals. Their molecules are made of pairs of atoms, and they have seven electrons in their outer shell.

As you move down the column, the elements become less reactive, with higher molecular masses, melting points and boiling points; the outermost shell is further away from the nucleus, making it difficult to attract and gain an electron.

Physical Properties

- Low melting and boiling points
- Poor conductors
- Coloured
- Form negative ions with a single negative charge
- Toxic

Fluorine   *Chlorine*

Astatine is highly radioactive and breaks down almost instantly, so its properties are uncertain.

Compounds

Halogens can share electrons via covalent bonding to form compounds with non-metals.

Hydrogen H_2 (g) + Chlorine Cl_2 (g) ⟶ Hydrogen chloride $2HCl$ (g)

Halogens react with metals to form ionic compounds called halide salts.

Chlorine Cl_2 (g) + Magnesium Mg (s) ⟶ Magnesium chloride $MgCl_2$ (s)

Displacement Reactions

A more reactive halogen can displace a less reactive halogen from a solution of its salt.

Chlorine Cl_2 (g) + Sodium bromide $2NaBr$ (aq) ⟶ Bromine Br_2 (aq) + Sodium chloride $2NaCl$ (aq)

For example, chlorine displaces bromine from sodium bromide solution. It also displaces iodine from potassium iodide solution. However, bromine and iodine cannot displace chlorine from sodium chloride because they are less reactive.

Separating Mixtures

Key Terminology

Pure substances
Pure substances are single elements or compounds, such as water. They are not mixed with anything else and cannot be separated by physical processes.

Mixtures
Mixtures consist of two or more elements or compounds. They are not chemically combined with each other and can be separated by physical processes.

Filtration

Filtration is used to separate insoluble solids from liquids (e.g. sand from water).

- Pour the mixture into the funnel.

- Filter paper contains tiny holes that allow water, but not sand, to pass.

- Sand gathers in the filter paper.

- Water flows through the funnel and gathers in the flask.

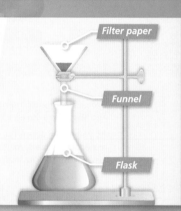

Filter paper

Funnel

Flask

Simple Distillation

Simple distillation is used to separate two liquids that have different boiling points (e.g. ethanol and water) or a solvent from a solution (e.g. water from salt).

- Heat the mixture until the substance with the lowest boiling point starts to boil and turn into a gas.

- The gas cools, condenses in the condenser and collects in the beaker. The rest of the mixture remains in the flask.

- The solution must be heated gradually so that the components of the mixture have time to evaporate at their respective boiling points.

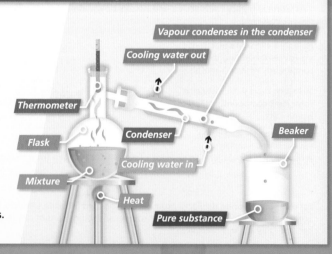

Vapour condenses in the condenser

Cooling water out

Thermometer

Flask

Condenser

Beaker

Cooling water in

Mixture

Heat

Pure substance

daydream
EDUCATION

Mixtures can be separated by physical processes. The type of separating technique you choose depends on the properties of the substances in the mixture.

Evaporation and Crystallisation

Evaporation and crystallisation are used to separate solutes (dissolved substances) from solutions (e.g. a salt from its solution).

Evaporating dish

- Place the solution in an evaporating dish and gently heat.

- The solvent will start to evaporate, leaving a more concentrated solution.

- When crystals start to form, remove the dish from the heat and leave to cool.

Heat

- Once the dish has cooled, filter out the crystals (if there is any liquid remaining) and leave to dry.

Paper Chromatography

Paper chromatography is used to separate solvents in a solution (e.g. different coloured dyes in an ink).

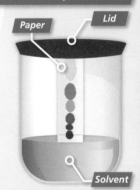

Paper   Lid

- Draw a line with a pencil at the bottom of a strip of paper, and add a spot of ink on the line.

- Place the paper into the solvent so the ink is above the surface of the solvent. It is important to choose a solvent that dissolves the ink.

- Place a lid on the beaker to stop the solvent from evaporating. The solvent then seeps up the paper from the bottom to the top, carrying the ink with it. The different dyes in the ink travel at different speeds so some move further than others in a given time. Therefore, each dye forms a spot in a different place on the paper.

Solvent

Fractional Distillation

Fractional distillation is used to separate complex mixtures (e.g. the fractions in crude oil).

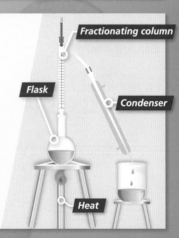

Fractionating column

Flask

Condenser

- Place the solution in a flask with a fractionating column attached on top, and heat the solution.

- The solvents have different boiling points and therefore boil at different temperatures. The liquid with the lowest boiling point will boil, turn into a gas and reach the top of the column first. The column is cooler at the top. Even if liquids with higher boiling points start to boil, they will condense before reaching the top of the column and run back down to the beaker.

- Once the first liquid has been collected, increase the temperature until the next liquid reaches its boiling point.

Heat

States of Matter

Particle theory is a basic model that helps to explain the properties and behaviour of materials in each of the three states. It enables us to visualise what is happening on a very small scale.

Solid

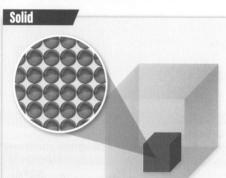

Particle Arrangement & Behaviour

- Strong forces of attraction between particles
- Usually in a regular arrangement
- Particles are close together and vibrate about fixed positions

Properties

- Has a definite shape
- Has a definite volume
- Usually has a high density
- Cannot easily be compressed

Liquid

Particle Arrangement & Behaviour

- Weak forces of attraction between particles
- Random arrangement
- Particles move about freely but are close together

Properties

- Takes the shape of its container
- Has a definite volume
- Cannot easily be compressed

Gas

Particle Arrangement & Behaviour

- Very weak forces of attraction between particles
- Random arrangement
- Particles move around freely and are far apart

Properties

- Takes the shape of its container
- Does not have a definite shape or volume
- Can easily be compressed

daydream EDUCATION

The three states of matter are solid, liquid and gas. In chemical equations, the three states of matter are shown as (s), (l) and (g) with (aq) for aqueous solutions.

Limitations Particle theory has some limitations as a model. For example, particles are not solid spheres, and the forces between the particles are not represented in the model.

State Changes – *Most substances can exist in all three states.*

The amount of energy needed to change state – from solid to liquid and from liquid to gas – depends on the strength of the forces between particles in a substance. The stronger the forces, the higher the melting point and boiling point of the substance.

State changes are physical changes that can be reversed. The chemical composition of the particles remains the same, but their arrangement, movement and amount of energy change.

 Boiling and evaporation are both changes of state from liquid to gas. Evaporation takes place at any temperature, but boiling occurs only at the boiling point.

Solid	**Melting:** when a solid changes into a liquid	**Liquid**	**Boiling/Evaporation:** when a liquid changes into a gas	**Gas**

 **Heat in** / **Heat out**

Ice (10 grams)	**Freezing:** when a liquid changes into a solid	**Water** (10 grams)	**Condensation:** when a gas changes into a liquid	**Steam** (10 grams)

Ionic Bonding

Ions are electrically charged particles. They are formed when atoms lose or gain electrons in an attempt to gain a full outer shell of electrons.

Ionic bonding occurs in compounds formed from metals combined with non-metals. Electrons in the outer shell of metal atoms are transferred to non-metal atoms to form a more stable electronic configuration.

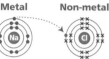

Metal   Non-metal

Sodium atom   Chlorine atom

Examples of Ionic Compounds

- Sodium chloride (NaCl)
- Magnesium oxide (MgO)
- Potassium sulfide (K_2S)

When metal ions form, the metal atoms lose electrons to become positively charged ions (cations).

The oppositely charged ions form ionic bonds.

When non-metal ions form, the non-metal atoms gain one or more electrons to become negatively charged ions (anions).

By transferring electrons during a chemical reaction, atoms gain a full outer shell of electrons and become stable.

The charge on an ion relates to how many electrons it needs to gain or lose to have a full outer shell of electrons. The charge of the ions produced by metals in groups 1 and 2 and by non-metals in groups 6 and 7 relates to the group number of the element in the periodic table.

Group	Electrons in Outer Shell	Gain/Lose Electrons	Ions Formed	Example	
Group 1	1	Lose 1 electron	1+ ions	Sodium	$Na \Rightarrow Na^+ + e^-$
Group 2	2	Lose 2 electrons	2+ ions	Magnesium	$Mg \Rightarrow Mg^{2+} + 2e^-$
Group 6	6	Gain 2 electrons	2– ions	Oxide	$O + 2e^- \Rightarrow O^{2-}$
Group 7	7	Gain 1 electron	1– ions	Chloride	$Cl + e^- \Rightarrow Cl^-$

The ions produced by metals in groups 1 and 2 and by non-metals in groups 6 and 7 have the electronic structure of a noble gas (group 0).

Example

In this example, the sodium atom loses an electron to become a Na^+ ion, and the chlorine atom gains an electron to become a Cl^- ion.

Each atom now has eight electrons in its outer shell and becomes stable.

The oppositely charged ions are strongly attracted by electrostatic forces and form an ionic bond.

The electron transfer in ionic bonding can be represented by a dot-and-cross diagram.

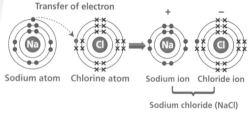

Transfer of electron

Sodium atom   Chlorine atom   Sodium ion   Chloride ion

Sodium chloride (NaCl)

$$Na^{\cdot} + {\cdot}\ddot{\underset{\cdot\cdot}{Cl}}{:} \Rightarrow [Na]^+ \ [:\ddot{\underset{\cdot\cdot}{Cl}}:]^-$$

(2,8,1)   (2,8,7)   (2,8)   (2,8,8)

Examples of Ionic Bonding

Here are some other examples of ionic bonding (with only the outer shell displayed):

Magnesium Oxide (MgO)

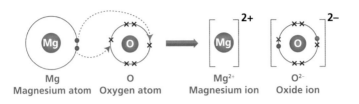

Mg
Magnesium atom | O
Oxygen atom | Mg^{2+}
Magnesium ion | O^{2-}
Oxide ion

The magnesium atom loses two electrons to become a Mg^{2+} ion, and the oxygen atom gains two electrons to become an O^{2-} ion.

Magnesium Fluoride (MgF$_2$)

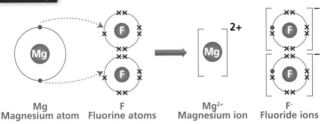

Mg
Magnesium atom | F
Fluorine atoms | Mg^{2+}
Magnesium ion | F^-
Fluoride ions

The magnesium atom loses two electrons to become a Mg^{2+} ion, and the fluorine atoms gain one electron each to become two F^- ions.

Iron Oxide (Fe$_2$O$_3$)

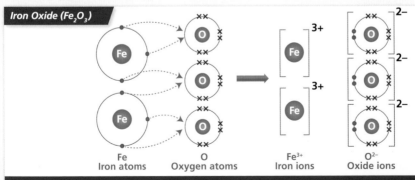

Fe
Iron atoms | O
Oxygen atoms | Fe^{3+}
Iron ions | O^{2-}
Oxide ions

The iron atoms lose three electrons to become Fe^{3+} ions, and the oxygen atoms gain two electrons each to become three O^{2-} ions.

Ionic Compounds

Ionic compounds have a giant ionic lattice structure and contain positively charged metal ions and negatively charged non-metal ions. There are strong electrostatic forces of attraction between the oppositely charged ions.

These are two ways of representing the giant ionic structure of sodium chloride:

Ball and Stick

The ball-and-stick diagram shows the arrangement of the ions. However, it is not completely accurate because the ions do not actually have gaps between them.

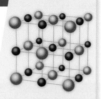

3D Model

The 3D model shows the arrangement of the ions more accurately than the ball-and-stick model, but the structure is less clear because only the outer layers can be clearly seen.

Key Na^+ Cl^-

It can be difficult to work out the formula of an ionic compound based on the above diagrams. However, it is possible to use the charges on the ions to determine the formula because the charges must balance in the formula.

Sodium Chloride

Sodium chloride is made from Na^+ and Cl^- ions. As each ion has one charge, one Na^+ is balanced by one Cl^-. The formula is NaCl.

Compound	Formula	Ions
Sodium chloride	NaCl	Na^+ Cl^-

- Sodium is found in Group 1. Its ions have a +1 charge.
- Chlorine is found in Group 7. Its ions have a –1 charge.
- The ratio of Na:Cl ions in the compound is 1:1.
- These charges are balanced, so the overall charge is neutral.

Magnesium Fluoride

In magnesium fluoride, the magnesium ions are Mg^{2+}. So two F^- ions are needed for balance. The formula is MgF_2.

- Magnesium is found in Group 2. Its ions have a +2 charge.
- Fluorine is found in Group 7. Its ions have a –1 charge.
- The ratio of Mg:F ions in the compound is 1:2.
- These charges are balanced, so the overall charge is neutral.

Compound	Formula	Ions
Magnesium fluoride	MgF_2	Mg^{2+} F^-

Properties of Ionic Compounds

High melting and boiling points	A lot of energy is needed to break the many ionic bonds in the giant lattice structure.
Brittle	If the structure of the lattice is displaced by force, similarly charged ions may align and repel each other, causing the structure to shatter.
Conduct electricity when molten or in solution	When melted or in solution, ions are free to move and therefore conduct electricity.

daydream
EDUCATION

Covalent Bonding

Covalent bonding occurs in most non-metallic elements and in compounds of non-metals.

In covalent bonding, pairs of electrons are shared to form very strong bonds. The positively charged nuclei of the atoms are attracted to the negative shared electrons.

By sharing electrons, atoms gain a full outer shell of electrons and become stable.

The sharing of electrons in covalent bonding can be represented by a dot-and-cross diagram.

In this example, both the hydrogen and chlorine atoms need one electron to become stable (i.e. to have a full outer shell of electrons).

Therefore, the hydrogen and chlorine atoms share a pair of electrons in their outer shell.

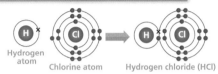

Hydrogen atom   Chlorine atom   Hydrogen chloride (HCl)

Covalent bonding can also be represented in other ways. Look at how ammonia (NH_3) is represented:

Molecules are formed through covalent bonding. The electron arrangement of some simple molecules joined by covalent bonds are shown below.

Hydrogen

Hydrogen atoms have only one electron, so two hydrogen atoms share a pair of electrons in a single bond to form a hydrogen molecule (H_2).

Chlorine

Chlorine atoms need one electron to gain a full outer shell, so two chlorine atoms share a pair of electrons in a single bond to form a chlorine molecule (Cl_2).

Nitrogen

Nitrogen atoms need three electrons to gain a full outer shell, so two nitrogen atoms share three pairs of electrons in a triple bond to form a nitrogen molecule (N_2).

Oxygen

Oxygen atoms need two electrons to gain a full outer shell, so two oxygen atoms share two pairs of electrons in a double bond to form an oxygen molecule (O_2).

Methane

A carbon atom forms four bonds with four hydrogen atoms to form a methane molecule (CH_4).

Water

An oxygen molecule forms two bonds with two hydrogen atoms to form a water molecule (H_2O).

Covalent Compounds

Covalent compounds contain non-metal atoms bonded together.

Carbon Monoxide (CO)

(*Mono-* means one.)

Carbon Dioxide (CO₂)

(*Di-* means two.)

Water (H₂O)

Hydrogen Chloride (HCl)

Methane (CH₄)

Ammonia (NH₃)

Many covalent compounds have small molecules that are gases or liquids at room temperature.

Properties of Small Molecules

Although there are strong covalent bonds between the atoms in small molecules, the intermolecular forces are weak. Therefore, they have relatively low melting points and boiling points and are easy to separate.

Intermolecular forces increase with the size of molecules, so larger molecules have higher melting and boiling points.

Because the atoms in small molecules are joined by covalent bonds, they do not have an electrical charge. There are no free electrons to carry a charge, so they do not conduct electricity.

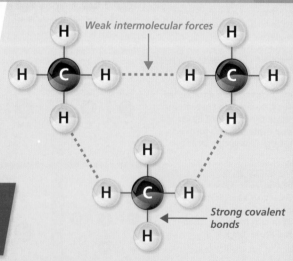

Weak intermolecular forces

Strong covalent bonds

daydream EDUCATION

Polymers & Giant Covalent Structures

Polymers and giant covalent structures are joined together by covalent bonds.

Polymers

A polymer is a very large molecule made from smaller molecules or atoms, called monomers, linked by covalent bonds. They have relatively strong intermolecular forces so are solids at room temperature.

The polymer poly(ethene) is made up of lots of ethene monomers.

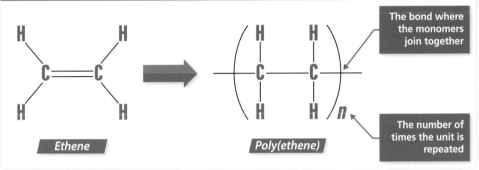

The bond where the monomers join together

The number of times the unit is repeated

Ethene

Poly(ethene)

Notice that the carbon atoms in the monomer have a double covalent bond but only a single covalent bond in the polymer.

Giant Covalent Structures

In a giant covalent structure, all the atoms are linked to other atoms by strong covalent bonds. A huge amount of energy is required to break the bonds. Therefore, these structures are solids with very high melting and boiling points.

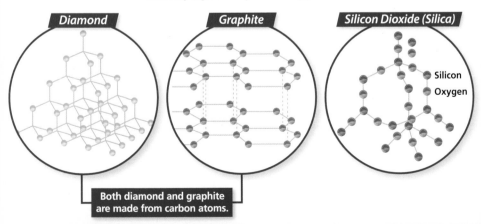

Diamond

Graphite

Silicon Dioxide (Silica)

Silicon
Oxygen

Both diamond and graphite are made from carbon atoms.

Most substances that have giant covalent structures do not conduct electricity in any state because they have no free electrons or ions to carry charge (graphite is an exception).

daydream
EDUCATION

Forms of Carbon

Diamond, graphite, graphene and fullerenes are examples of giant covalent structures that are made of only carbon atoms. Their properties relate to their structure.

Diamond

In diamond, each carbon atom forms four covalent bonds with other carbon atoms.

Because of its hardness, diamond is often used to strengthen cutting tools.

Properties	Relation to Structure
Very hard	Diamond has a rigid lattice structure, with strong bonds that are hard to break.
High melting point	A lot of energy is needed to break the strong covalent bonds.
Does not conduct electricity	All the outer electrons are used in the covalent bonds and are not free to move.

Graphite

In graphite, each carbon atom forms three covalent bonds with other carbon atoms. The atoms form layers of hexagonal rings that are held together by weak forces. Each carbon atom has one delocalised electron that is free to move around.

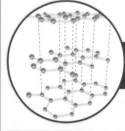

Graphite is often used as a lubricant because of its slipperiness. It is also used in electrodes because of its electrical conductivity.

Properties	Relation to Structure
Soft and slippery	Weak forces between the layers allow them to break and slide over each other.
High melting point	A lot of energy is needed to break all the bonds.
Conducts electricity	The delocalised electrons are free to move.

daydream EDUCATION

Graphene

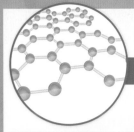

Graphene is a single layer of graphite.

Properties	Use Based on This Property	Relation to Structure
Very strong	Makes composite materials stronger	Strong covalent bonds exist between all atoms.
Transparent	Touchscreen devices	It is only one atom thick.
Conducts electricity	Electronics	Delocalised electrons are free to move.

Fullerenes

Fullerenes are molecules of carbon atoms with hollow shapes such as spheres and tubes. They are mainly composed of hexagonal rings of carbon atoms but can also contain rings with five or seven carbon atoms.

This was the first fullerene to be discovered.

Cylindrical fullerenes have very high length-to-diameter ratios.

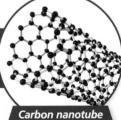

Buckminsterfullerene (C_{60})

Carbon nanotube

Properties	Use Based on This Property
Hollow shape	Carries drug molecules around the body
High tensile strength	Reinforces materials (e.g. in tennis rackets)
High electrical conductivity	Used as a semiconductor in electrical circuits
Large surface area	Helps make catalysts

Metallic Bonding & Properties of Metals & Alloys

Metallic Bonding

Metallic bonding occurs in metallic elements and alloys.

Metals consist of closely packed, positively charged metal ions arranged in a regular pattern and a 'sea' of negatively charged, delocalised electrons.

The electrons in the outer shell of the metal atoms are free to move through the whole structure.

The electrostatic forces between these electrons and the metal ions give rise to strong metallic bonds.

Examples of Metals

- Iron
- Copper
- Steel
- Bronze

Free electrons

Metal ions

The bonding in metals can be represented in the following forms:

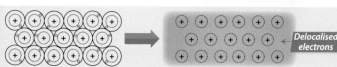

Delocalised electrons

The Properties of Metals & Alloys

The strong metallic bonds between the atoms in metals usually give them high melting and boiling points (mercury is an exception).

Metals are generally good conductors of electricity due to the ability of their delocalised electrons to move and carry electrical charge through the substance. They can also collide and transfer energy, so they are good conductors of heat.

Force

It is relatively easy to distort metals as the layers of atoms can slide over each other whilst still maintaining their bond. Therefore, most metals are malleable (can be bent and shaped).

This property means that pure metals are too soft for many uses and therefore are mixed with other elements, mainly metals, to make harder alloys.

Alloys

An alloy is a mixture of elements, usually metals. They have metallic bonds, but due to the different sizes of the atoms, the layers are distorted, which makes the substance much harder and more difficult to shape.

Brass

(copper and zinc)

Stainless Steel

(iron, carbon and a minimum of 10.5% chromium)

High Speed Steel

(various elements including carbon, tungsten and chromium)

daydream
EDUCATION

Relative Formula Mass & Conservation of Mass

Relative Formula Mass

The relative formula mass (M_r) of a compound is the sum of the relative atomic masses (A_r) of the atoms in the compound. Remember, relative atomic mass is the average mass of atoms of an element based on the abundance of each isotope that exists.

In a balanced chemical equation, the sum of the relative formula masses of the reactants must equal the sum of the relative formula masses of the products.

Compound	Formula	A_r of Atoms	M_r
Carbon dioxide	CO_2	C = 12, O = 16	12 + (2 × 16) = 44
Iron chloride	$FeCl_3$	Fe = 55.8, Cl = 35.5	55.8 + (3 × 35.5) = 162.3
Calcium sulfate	$CaSO_4$	Ca = 40, S = 32, O = 16	40 + 32 + (4 × 16) = 136
Magnesium nitrate	$Mg(NO_3)_2$	Mg = 24, N = 14, O = 16	24 + (2 × 14) + (6 × 16) = 148

Conservation of Mass & Balancing Chemical Equations

During a chemical reaction, no atoms are made or lost, so the mass of the products will always equal the mass of the reactants. This is known as conservation of mass. It also means that there are the same type and number of atoms before and after a chemical reaction has taken place.

Symbol equations show the number of atoms involved in a chemical reaction.

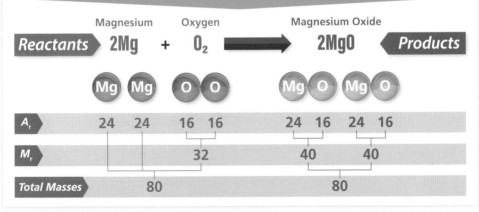

The number of oxygen and magnesium atoms is the same on both sides, so the equation is balanced. The total masses on both sides of the equation must also balance.

When Mass Appears to Change

The law of conservation of mass indicates that the mass of the products must always equal the mass of the reactants. However, reactions often seem to involve a change in mass. This is usually because a reactant or product is a gas, and its mass has not been included.

Copper reacts with oxygen to form copper oxide.	Calcium carbonate is broken down by heat to form calcium oxide and carbon dioxide.
The mass of copper oxide will be greater than that of the copper because oxygen has been added to it.	The mass of calcium oxide is less than that of the calcium carbonate because mass has been lost from the system as carbon dioxide.

$$2Cu + O_2 \longrightarrow 2CuO \qquad CaCO_3 \longrightarrow CaO + CO_2$$

Measurements and Uncertainty

Scientific results hardly ever turn out exactly the same when you repeat measurements. This can be due to random error or limits to the resolution of the instruments used. Every measurement you make has a level of uncertainty. How big this uncertainty is varies depending on the situation.

The resolution of an instrument is the smallest change it can detect.

Calculating the Uncertainty of Mean Results

The uncertainty of a mean can be calculated from the range using this formula:

$$uncertainty = \frac{range}{2}$$

Uncertainty can be reduced by doing more repeats or samples. The greater the uncertainty, the less confidence you can have in the accuracy of your results.

Precision relates to the range of the results. Results with a small range are called precise.

daydream
EDUCATION

Moles

Chemical amounts are measured in moles. The symbol for the unit mole is mol.

A mole of a substance is a mass, and it varies from one substance to another. It is the relative formula mass (M_r) in grams. Moles can apply to atoms, molecules, ions and electrons.

The M_r of potassium (K) is 39 so 1 mole of potassium is 39 g.

The M_r of nitrogen (N_2) is 28 so 1 mole of nitrogen is 28 g.

The M_r of sulfuric acid (H_2SO_4) is 98 so 1 mole of sulfuric acid is 98 g.

Remember, M_r is an average mass for all the isotopes of an element.

The Avogadro Constant

One mole of any given substance will always contain the same number of particles (atoms, molecules or ions, depending on the substance) as one mole of any other substance. That number is called the Avogadro constant, and its value is 6.02×10^{23}.

For example, 1 mole of carbon (an atom) contains the same number of atoms as there are molecules in 1 mole of carbon dioxide (a molecule):

$$6.02 \times 10^{23}$$

Calculating the Number of Moles in a Given Mass

The number of moles in a given mass can be calculated using the following equation:

moles (mol)   grams (g)

$$\text{Number of moles} = \frac{\text{mass}}{M_r}$$

How many moles are there in 32 g of sulfur dioxide (SO_2)?

$$\text{number of moles} = \frac{\text{mass}}{M_r}$$

$$M_r = 32 + (2 \times 16)$$
$$= 64$$

$$\text{number of moles} = \frac{32}{64}$$

$$= 0.5 \text{ mol}$$

Calculate the mass of 10 moles of carbon dioxide (CO_2).

$$\text{mass} = \text{number of moles} \times M_r$$

$$\text{mass} = 10 \times 44$$

$$= 440 \text{ g}$$

$$M_r = 12 + (2 \times 16)$$
$$= 44$$

Moles in Equations

The masses of reactants and products can be calculated using balanced equations.

$$Mg + 2HCl \longrightarrow MgCl_2 + H_2$$

This equation shows that one mole of magnesium reacts with two moles of hydrochloric acid to form one mole of magnesium chloride and one mole of hydrogen.

Relative atomic masses: $Mg = 24$ $Cl = 35.5$ $H = 1$

Using the relative atomic masses of the elements involved, we can calculate that:

24 g of magnesium (1 mole) will react with 73 g of hydrochloric acid (2 moles) to form 95 g of magnesium chloride (1 mole) and 2 g of hydrogen (1 mole).

Mg +	$2HCl$	$\longrightarrow$	$MgCl_2$	+	H_2
24 +	$(2 \times 1) + (2 \times 35.5)$		$24 + (35.5 \times 2)$	+	(1×2)
24 +	73		95	+	2

Calculating the Mass of a Product from the Mass of a Reactant

Using the same equation, we can calculate how much magnesium chloride will be produced if we use a given mass of hydrochloric acid by converting the mass into moles.

What mass of magnesium chloride is produced when 50 g of hydrochloric acid is mixed with magnesium?

1	Calculate the mass of 1 mole of HCl.	$1 + 35.5 = 36.5$ g
2	Calculate the number of moles in 50 g of HCl.	number of moles $= \dfrac{50}{36.5} = 1.37$ mol
3	Each mole of HCl produces 0.5 mol of $MgCl_2$.	2 mol of HCl produce 1 mol of $MgCl_2$, so 1 mol will produce 0.5 mol.
4	Calculate how much $MgCl_2$ will be produced by 1.37 moles of HCl.	$0.5 \times 1.37 = 0.685$ mol
5	Calculate the mass of 1 mole of $MgCl_2$.	$24 + 35.5 + 35.5 = 95$ g
6	Calculate the mass of 0.685 mol of $MgCl_2$.	$0.685 \times 95 = 65.08$ g

Assuming that there is enough magnesium for the hydrochloric acid to react with, 50 g of HCl will produce 65.08 g of $MgCl_2$.

We can use the same method in reverse to calculate how much of a reactant will be needed to produce a given mass of product.

$$2Mg \quad + \quad O_2 \quad \longrightarrow \quad 2MgO$$

Calculate the mass of oxygen needed to form 20 g of magnesium oxide.

1	Calculate the mass of 1 mole of MgO.	$24 + 16 = 40$ g
2	Calculate the number of moles in 20 g of MgO.	number of moles $= \dfrac{20}{40} = 0.5$ mol
3	Each mole of O_2 produces 2 moles of MgO.	
4	Calculate how many moles of O_2 will be needed to produce 0.5 mol of MgO.	$0.5 \div 2 = 0.25$ mol
5	Calculate the mass of 1 mole of O_2.	$16 + 16 = 32$ g
6	Calculate the mass of 0.25 mol of O_2.	$32 \times 0.25 = 8$ g

Assuming that there is enough magnesium for the oxygen to react with, 20 g of MgO will be produced by 8 g of O_2.

daydream EDUCATION

The balancing numbers in a symbol equation can be calculated from the masses of reactants and products. The masses (in grams) are converted to moles, and then the numbers of moles are converted into simple whole number ratios.

This is the reverse process of calculating masses of reactants and products from an equation.

Example

6 g of magnesium reacts with 18.25 g of hydrochloric acid to produce 23.75 g of magnesium chloride and 0.5 g of hydrogen.

1 Calculate the moles for each substance.	**Mg:** no. of moles = $\dfrac{6}{24}$ = 0.25 mol **HCl:** no. of moles = $\dfrac{18.25}{36.5}$ = 0.5 mol **$MgCl_2$:** no. of moles = $\dfrac{23.75}{95}$ = 0.25 mol **H:** no. of moles = $\dfrac{0.5}{2}$ = 0.25 mol
2 Calculate the simplest whole number ratios for the substances in the reaction.	The ratio of the chemicals is: 0.25 Mg : 0.5 HCl : 0.25 $MgCl_2$: 0.25 H_2 The ratio whole numbers are: 1 Mg : 2 HCl : 1 $MgCl_2$: 1 H_2
3 Therefore the equation is:	Mg + $2HCl$ ⟶ $MgCl_2$ + H_2

Limiting Reactants

In a chemical reaction involving two reactants, it is common to use an excess of one of the reactants so that all the other reactant is used. The reactant that is completely consumed is called the limiting reactant because it is the one that limits the amount of the products.

Calculating the Concentration of Solutions

The concentration of a solution can be measured by calculating the mass of the solute per given volume of solution, often in grams per cubic decimetre (g/dm^3).

$$concentration = \frac{mass\ of\ solute}{volume}$$

Often you will need to covert the volume from cm^3 to dm^3 ($1\ dm^3 = 1,000\ cm^3$).

1	A student adds 10 g of sodium carbonate to 300 cm^3 of water. What is the concentration of the solution obtained?	300 cm^3 = 0.3 dm^3 concentration = $\dfrac{10}{0.3}$ = 33.3 g The concentration is 33.3 g/dm^3.
2	A solution of sodium chloride has a concentration of 70 g/dm^3. What mass of sodium chloride is in 200 cm^3 of this solution?	70 g/dm^3 = $\dfrac{mass}{0.2}$ mass = 70 × 0.2 = 14 g The solution has 14 g of sodium chloride.

Reactivity of Metals

The Reactivity Series

The reactivity series lists metals in order of their reactivity.

The ease by which metals lose electrons determines their level of reactivity.

Metals higher up the reactivity series have a greater tendency to lose electrons and form positive ions. Therefore, they are more reactive.

Carbon and hydrogen are not metals, but they are often included in the reactivity series to show how metals in the series can be extracted from their ores. This is explained in more detail in the **Metal Extraction** section.

Potassium	K	
Sodium	Na	
Lithium	Li	
Calcium	Ca	
Magnesium	Mg	
Carbon	C	
Zinc	Zn	
Iron	Fe	
Hydrogen	H	
Copper	Cu	

Non-metals

Increased reactivity

Oxidation and Reduction

Reactions of metals often involve the processes of oxidation and reduction.

Oxidation is the addition of oxygen or the removal of electrons.

Reduction is the removal of oxygen or the addition of electrons.

Displacement Reactions

A more reactive metal can displace a less reactive metal from a compound.

Example: If iron is placed in a copper sulfate solution, the iron will displace the copper to form iron sulfate.

iron
Fe
+
copper sulfate
$CuSO_4$

iron sulfate
$FeSO_4$
+
copper
Cu

This is an example of a redox reaction in which one substance is reduced and another is oxidised.

In this reaction, the iron atoms are oxidised to form iron ions, and the copper ions are reduced to form copper atoms. The iron atoms lose two electrons (oxidation), whereas the copper ions gain two electrons (reduction).

$$Fe \longrightarrow Fe^{2+} + 2e^-$$

$$Cu^{2+} + 2e^- \longrightarrow Cu$$

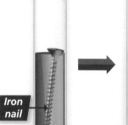

Iron nail

Copper forms on nail

Blue copper sulfate solution

Green iron sulfate solution

daydream
EDUCATION

Reactions with Acids and Water

The higher a metal is in the reactivity series, the more easily it will react with dilute acids and water. In all reactions, the metal atoms lose electrons to form positive ions.

metal + acid = salt + hydrogen

metal + water = metal hydroxide + hydrogen

Reaction with Dilute Acids	Element	Symbol	Reaction with Water
React vigorously to form a salt solution and hydrogen	Potassium	K	React quickly to form a metal hydroxide and hydrogen
	Sodium	Na	
	Lithium	Li	
React more slowly to form a salt solution and hydrogen	Calcium	Ca	React slowly or not at all with cold water; form hydrogen and a metal oxide with steam
	Magnesium	Mg	
	Zinc	Zn	
	Iron	Fe	
No reaction	Copper	Cu	No reaction

Metal Extraction

Carbon and hydrogen are often included in the reactivity series to show how metals can be extracted from their ores. For example, metals such as zinc can be displaced by adding carbon, whereas copper can be displaced by adding carbon or hydrogen.

Metals that are more reactive than carbon, such as aluminium, have to be extracted from their ores using a process called electrolysis. Unreactive metals such as gold and platinum are found as pure elements and do not need to be extracted.

Many metals react with oxygen to form metal oxides (ores) in a process called oxidation. Therefore, to extract a metal from its ore, oxygen needs to be removed in a process called reduction.

The Blast Furnace

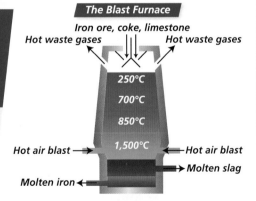

Iron ore, coke, limestone
Hot waste gases — Hot waste gases
250°C
700°C
850°C
Hot air blast → 1,500°C ← Hot air blast
→ Molten slag
Molten iron ←

Iron is extracted from iron oxide by heating it with carbon in a blast furnace. Because carbon is more reactive than iron, it displaces the iron from the iron oxide.

iron oxide	+	carbon		iron	+	carbon dioxide
$2Fe_2O_3$		$3C$	$\longrightarrow$	$4Fe$		$3CO_2$

Iron oxide is reduced (loses oxygen) to form iron.
Carbon is oxidised (gains oxygen) to form carbon dioxide.

daydream
EDUCATION

Acids and Alkalis

The pH scale is a measure of the acidity or alkalinity of a solution. It can be measured by a universal indicator, which changes colour depending on the pH of the solution. The colours for each pH are shown below. A digital pH probe and meter can also be used to measure the pH of a solution.

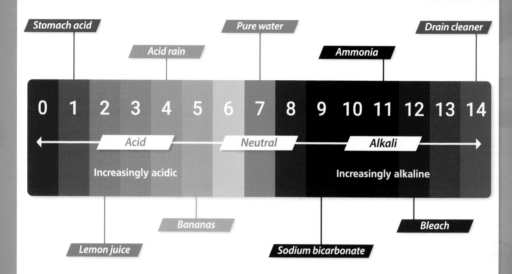

A base is a substance that neutralises an acid. An alkali is a soluble base. All alkalis are bases, but not all bases are alkalis.

Acids produce an excess of hydrogen ions (H^+) in aqueous solutions (aq).

As the number of hydrogen ions in a certain volume increases, the lower the pH level and the more acidic the solution.

When acids and alkalis react, hydrogen ions react with hydroxide ions to produce water. This is called neutralisation.

$$\text{acid} + \text{alkali} \longrightarrow \text{water}$$
$$H^+_{(aq)} \quad OH^-_{(aq)} \quad H_2O_{(l)}$$

Alkalis produce an excess of hydroxide ions (OH^-) in aqueous solutions (aq).

As the number of hydroxide ions in a certain volume increases, the higher the pH level and the more alkaline the solution.

The pH scale is a measure of the concentration of hydrogen ions in a solution. As the pH level increases by one unit, the hydrogen ion concentration of the solution decreases by a factor of 10.

pH: 0 1 2 3 4
H^+: ÷10 ÷10 ÷10 ÷10

daydream EDUCATION

Reactions of Acids

Acids react with metals to produce salts and hydrogen. The salt that is produced in any reaction depends on the **acid used** and the positive ions in the metal or base.

---

acid + metal ➡ salt + hydrogen

acid + metal hydroxide ➡ salt + water

acid + metal oxide ➡ salt + water

Hydrochloric acid produces chlorides:

$$\text{hydrochloric acid} + \text{magnesium} \longrightarrow \text{magnesium chloride} + \text{hydrogen}$$
$$2HCl \qquad\qquad Mg \qquad\qquad\qquad MgCl_2 \qquad\qquad H_2$$

Nitric acid produces nitrates:

$$\text{nitric acid} + \text{sodium hydroxide} \longrightarrow \text{sodium nitrate} + \text{water}$$
$$HNO_3 \qquad\qquad NaOH \qquad\qquad\qquad NaNO_3 \qquad\qquad H_2O$$

Sulfuric acid produces sulfates:

$$\text{sulfuric acid} + \text{copper oxide} \longrightarrow \text{copper sulfate} + \text{water}$$
$$H_2SO_4 \qquad\qquad CuO \qquad\qquad\qquad CuSO_4 \qquad\qquad H_2O$$

Metal carbonates neutralise acids to produce salt, water and carbon dioxide.

acid + metal carbonate ➡ salt + water + carbon dioxide

$$\text{sulfuric acid} + \text{copper carbonate} \longrightarrow \text{copper sulfate} + \text{water} + \text{carbon dioxide}$$
$$H_2SO_4 \qquad\qquad CuCO_3 \qquad\qquad\qquad CuSO_4 \qquad\qquad H_2O \qquad\qquad CO_2$$

You can make a soluble salt by neutralising an acid with a base, such as an insoluble metal oxide, hydroxide or carbonate.

Step 1

Gently heat the acid, add the insoluble base and stir.

Step 2

Keep adding the base until there is no more reaction. This means there is excess base.

Step 3

Filter out the excess base from the solution.

Step 4

Heat the solution to evaporate some of the water. Then leave it to cool to allow salt crystals to form.

The reactions between acids and metals are redox reactions. The metal loses electrons and so is oxidised. The hydrogen gains electrons and so is reduced.

When magnesium reacts with hydrochloric acid, the magnesium is oxidised (loses electrons), forming magnesium chloride, whereas the hydrochloric acid is reduced (gaining electrons), forming hydrogen gas.

$$Mg \longrightarrow Mg^{2+} + 2e^-$$

$$2H^+ + 2e^- \longrightarrow H_2$$

$$Mg + 2H\text{-}Cl \longrightarrow Mg^{2+}Cl^-_2 + H_2$$

Strong and Weak Acids

All acids ionise (produce protons) in aqueous solution.

A strong acid is one that is completely ionised in aqueous solution, so it releases a lot of hydrogen (H$^+$) ions.

Examples include hydrochloric, sulfuric and nitric acids.

Weak acids are only partially ionised in aqueous solution. They are less reactive.

Examples include ethanoic, citric and carbonic acids.

 Hydrogen ion   Undissociated molecule

As pH decreases by one unit, the hydrogen ion concentration increases by a factor of 10.

Strong and weak are not the same as concentrated and dilute. A concentrated acid contains a high proportion of acid to water in the aqueous solution, whereas a dilute acid contains a lower proportion. Adding water to a strong acid dilutes it but does not turn it into a weak acid.

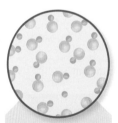

Weak, concentrated ethanoic acid

Weak, dilute ethanoic acid

Strong, concentrated hydrochloric acid

Strong, dilute hydrochloric acid

 Acid (CH$_3$COOH, HCL)   Conjugate base (CH$_3$COO$^-$(aq), Cl$^-$(aq))   ● H$^+$(aq)

daydream EDUCATION

Electrolysis

Electrolysis is the process by which ionic substances are decomposed (broken down) into simpler substances when an electric current is passed through them.

When an ionic compound is dissolved in water or melted to form an electrolyte, its ions are free to move about and conduct electricity. During electrolysis, an electric current is passed through the electrolyte to break it down into simpler substances.

- Electrodes are usually made of carbon (graphite).
- Electrodes are inert. This means they do not form ions during electrolysis.
- Ions are discharged (lose their charge) at the electrodes.

Don't PANIC!
Positive is Anode
Negative is Cathode

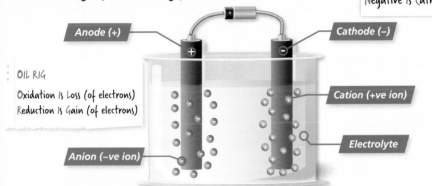

Anode (+)

Cathode (−)

OIL RIG
Oxidation is Loss (of electrons)
Reduction is Gain (of electrons)

Cation (+ve ion)

Electrolyte

Anion (−ve ion)

Negative Ions (Anions)

Negative ions (anions) are attracted to the positively charged anode, where they lose electrons to form atoms.

This is oxidation. It can be shown as a half-equation:

$$X^- - e^- \Rightarrow X \text{ or } X^- \Rightarrow X + e^-$$

Positive Ions (Cations)

Positive ions (cations) are attracted to the negatively charged cathode, where they gain electrons to form atoms.

This is reduction. It can be shown as a half-equation:

$$Y^+ + e^- \Rightarrow Y$$

Electrolysis of Molten Ionic Compounds

When a simple ionic compound is electrolysed in a molten state, the metal is always produced at the cathode and the non-metal is always produced at the anode.

lead (II) bromide $\Rightarrow$ lead + bromine

Bromine molecules (Br_2) formed at the anode:
$$2Br^- \Rightarrow Br_2 + 2e^-$$

Lead (Pb) atoms formed at the cathode:
$$Pb^{2+} + 2e^- \Rightarrow Pb$$

Molten lead (II) bromide

Negative bromide ions attracted to the positive electrode

Positive lead ions attracted to the negative electrode

Compound	Product at Cathode	Product at Anode
Sodium chloride (NaCl)	Sodium (Na)	Chlorine (Cl_2)
Magnesium oxide (MgO)	Magnesium (Mg)	Oxygen (O_2)

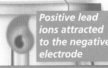

Electrolysis to Extract Metals

Metals above carbon in the reactivity series must be extracted by electrolysis. Electrolysis requires lots of energy to melt the compounds and to produce the electrical current, so it is very expensive.

It is used to extract aluminium from bauxite (aluminium oxide). **aluminium oxide ➡ aluminium + oxygen**

As bauxite has a very high melting point, it is dissolved in molten cryolite (another oxide of aluminium), which has a lower melting point.

Molten aluminium out

Positive electrodes (anodes)

The negative oxide ions are attracted to the anodes, where they lose electrons to form oxygen.

$$2O^{2-} \implies O_2 + 4e^-$$

Negative electrode (cathode)

The positive aluminium ions are attracted to the cathode, where they gain electrons to form aluminium.

$$Al^{3+} + 3e^- \implies Al$$

At the anode, the oxygen formed reacts with the carbon electrodes to form carbon dioxide. This means that the anodes frequently have to be replaced. $C(s) + O_2(g) \implies CO_2(g)$

Electrolysis of Aqueous Solutions

When an aqueous solution is electrolysed, the ions discharged depend on the reactivity of the elements involved. Hydrogen is produced at the cathode if the metal is more reactive than hydrogen. At the positive electrode, oxygen is produced unless the solution contains halide ions when the halogen is produced.

Copper Chloride Solution

When copper chloride dissolves in water, a mixture of ions is present.

The copper chloride breaks down into copper ions (Cu^{2+}) and chloride ions (Cl^-).

$$CuCl_2 \implies Cu^{2+} + 2Cl^-$$

The water molecules break down, producing hydrogen ions (H^+) and hydroxide ions (OH^-).

$$H_2O \implies H^+ + OH^-$$

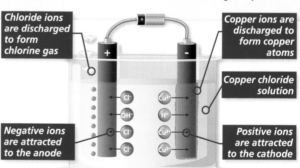

Chloride ions are discharged to form chlorine gas

Copper ions are discharged to form copper atoms

Copper chloride solution

Negative ions are attracted to the anode

Positive ions are attracted to the cathode

$$2Cl^- \implies Cl_2 + 2e^- \qquad Cu^{2+} + 2e^- \implies Cu$$

Aqueous Solution	Ions Present	At the Cathode	At the Anode
Sodium chloride (NaCl)	Na^+, Cl^-, H^+, OH^-	Sodium is more reactive than hydrogen, so hydrogen ions are discharged to form hydrogen: $2H^+ + 2e^- \implies H_2$	Chloride ions are discharged to form chlorine: $2Cl^- \implies Cl_2 + 2e^-$
Copper sulfate (CuSO$_4$)	Cu^{2+}, SO_4^{2-}, H^+, OH^-	Copper is less reactive than hydrogen, so copper ions are discharged to form copper: $Cu^{2+} + 2e^- \implies Cu$	No halide ions are present, so hydroxide ions are discharged to form water and oxygen: $4OH^- \implies O_2 + 2H_2O + 4e^-$

daydream EDUCATION

Exothermic & Endothermic Reactions

In chemical reactions, energy is conserved. This means that the amount of energy is the same at the end of a chemical reaction as it was before the reaction took place.

Exothermic Reactions

In an exothermic reaction, heat energy is given out, and the temperature of the surroundings increases.

The reactants have more energy than the products, so energy is given out.

Examples of exothermic reactions include combustion (burning), many oxidation reactions and neutralisation. Exothermic reactions are used in self-heating cans and hand warmers.

During exothermic reactions, the energy released through the formation of bonds is greater than the energy used to break bonds.

Heat

Endothermic Reactions

In an endothermic reaction, heat energy is taken in, and the temperature of the surroundings decreases.

The reactants have less energy than the products, so energy is taken in.

Examples of endothermic reactions include thermal decomposition and the reaction of citric acid and sodium hydrogen carbonate. Endothermic reactions are used in some sports injury cold packs.

During endothermic reactions, the energy used to break bonds is greater than the energy released through the formation of bonds.

Heat

Reaction Profiles

Chemical reactions occur only when particles collide with each other with sufficient energy. The minimum amount of energy that particles must have to react is called the activation energy.

Reaction profiles are used to show the relative energies of the reactants and products in a reaction and how energy changes during the reaction.

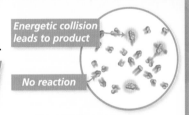

Energetic collision leads to product

No reaction

Exothermic Reaction Profile

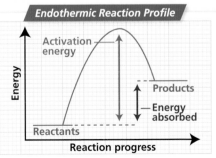

Activation energy

Reactants

Energy released

Products

Energy

Reaction progress

The products are at a lower energy level than the reactants.

Endothermic Reaction Profile

Activation energy

Products

Energy absorbed

Reactants

Energy

Reaction progress

The products are at a higher energy level than the reactants.

Measuring Energy Transfer

You can measure the amount of energy released in a chemical reaction (in solution) by measuring the temperature change during the reaction.

method

1 Add one reactant to the cup and measure the temperature.

2 Add the other reactant and mix.

3 Measure the temperature of the solution at the end of the reaction.

4 If the temperature increases, the reaction is exothermic. If it decreases, the reaction is endothermic.

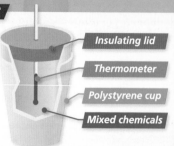

Insulating lid

Thermometer

Polystyrene cup

Mixed chemicals

The insulating lid and polystyrene cup help limit the amount of energy lost to the surroundings.

Bond Energies

When a chemical bond is formed, energy is released, making it an exothermic reaction. To break a bond, energy needs to be supplied, making it an endothermic reaction. Bond energies are different for different bonds.

The energy required to make a bond in a substance is the same as the energy required to break the same bond.

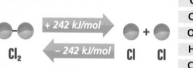

$+ 242$ kJ/mol

$- 242$ kJ/mol

Cl_2 Cl   Cl

Examples of Bond Energies

Bond	Bond Energy (kJ/mol)
H-H	436
C-H	413
C=O	743
O=O	496
H-Cl	432
Cl-Cl	242

Calculating Energy Change in a Reaction

You can use the different bond energies in a reaction to calculate the overall energy change. The difference between the sum of energy required to break bonds in the reactants and the sum of the energy released when bonds in the products are made is the overall energy change.

What is the overall energy change in the reaction of methane with oxygen to produce carbon dioxide and water?

Chemical equation

$$CH_4 + 2O_2 \longrightarrow CO_2 + 2H_2O$$

1	Identify the bond energies for each compound or molecule.	C-H = 413 kJ/mol C=O = 743 kJ/mol O=O = 496 kJ/mol O-H = 463 kJ/mol
2	Identify the number of bonds in the equation.	H H-C-H + O=O $\longrightarrow$ O=C=O + H-O-H H O=O H-O-H 4 × C-H 2 × O=O 2 × C=O 4 × O-H
3	Calculate the bond energies for the reactants and the products.	4 × 413 + 2 × 496 2 × 743 + 4 × 463 2,644 kJ/mol 3,338 kJ/mol
4	Calculate the energy change in the reaction.	energy to break bonds − energy to form bonds 2,644 − 3,338 = −694 kJ/mol

The overall energy change is −694 kJ/mol.
As more energy is released than is used, the reaction is exothermic.

daydream
EDUCATION

Rate of Reaction

Chemical reactions can occur at vastly different rates. The reactivity of the reactants is a major factor in determining the rate, but other variables also have an effect.

Calculating Rates of Reaction

The rate of a chemical reaction can be measured by measuring either the quantity of reactant used or the quantity of product formed over a given time.

$$\text{mean rate of reaction} = \frac{\text{quantity of reactant used}}{\text{time taken}}$$

$$\text{mean rate of reaction} = \frac{\text{quantity of product formed}}{\text{time taken}}$$

The quantity of reactant used or product formed is usually measured in mass (g) or by volume (cm^3). Therefore, the unit for the rate of reaction is either g/s or cm^3/s.

Quantities are also measured in moles, with the rate of reaction unit being mol/s.

The measurements are means because the reaction rate often varies during the time taken.

The rate of a reaction can be measured in various ways, including:

Volume of gas collected per unit time	Time taken for a colour change or a change in turbidity	Increase in temperature per unit time in the reaction mixture (for exothermic reactions)	Decrease in mass of a reactant or increase in mass of a product per unit time

Rates of Reaction Graphs

Graphs can be created to show the quantity of a reactant consumed or the quantity of a product formed against time. The example below shows the quantity of a product formed against time.

The steeper the line of the graph, the faster the rate of reaction. Over time, the line will generally get shallower as more of the reactants are consumed.

The reaction represented by the blue line produces the most amount of product. It starts off relatively quickly and finishes the latest.

The reaction represented by the green line produces the second most amount of product. It starts off the fastest and ends the quickest.

The reaction represented by the orange line produces the least amount of product. It starts off the slowest and finishes relatively quickly.

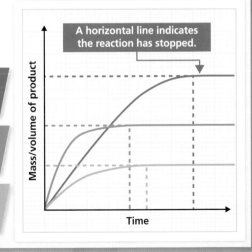

A horizontal line indicates the reaction has stopped.

Mass/volume of product

Time

Calculating Rates of Reaction Using Graphs

The rate of reaction between two times can be calculated using a graph. Simply divide the change in values on the y-axis by the change in values on the x-axis.

The graph below shows the volume of gas produced in an experiment over a period of time. Calculate the mean rate of reaction between 10 and 30 seconds.

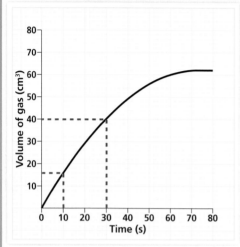

1 Find 10 seconds and 30 seconds on the x-axis, and draw lines up to the rate of reaction line.

2 From the points where these lines touch the rate of reaction line, draw horizontal lines to the y-axis.

3 Calculate the rate of reaction.

$$\text{mean rate of reaction} = \frac{\text{change in } y}{\text{change in } x}$$

$$= \frac{40 - 16}{30 - 10}$$

$$= \frac{24}{20}$$

$$= 1.2 \text{ cm}^3/s$$

The rate of reaction at a specific time can also be measured by calculating the gradient of a tangent to the curve on the graph.

The graph below shows the volume of gas produced in an experiment over a period of time. Calculate the rate of reaction at 30 seconds.

1 Find the point on the line that aligns vertically with 30 seconds on the x-axis.

2 Place your ruler on the line, and draw a tangent to this point (30 seconds). (Ensure the tangent extends across the graph.)

3 Pick two points on the tangent and calculate its gradient.

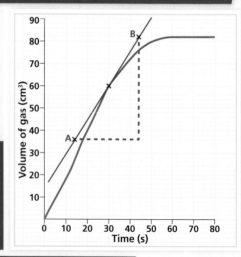

$$\text{gradient} = \frac{\text{change in } y}{\text{change in } x}$$

$$= \frac{82 - 36}{44 - 14}$$

$$= \frac{46}{30}$$

$$= 1.53 \text{ cm}^3/s \text{ (2 d.p.)}$$

The rate of reaction at 30 seconds was 1.53 cm³/s.

daydream
EDUCATION

Collision Theory

Collision theory states that chemical reactions happen when reactant particles collide, as long as there is sufficient energy to start a reaction. The minimum amount of energy needed to start a given reaction is called the activation energy.

A certain proportion of collisions will be 'successful collisions' – that is, they will have enough energy to cause a reaction.

There are various factors that can increase the frequency of collisions, the number of successful collisions and the reaction rate.

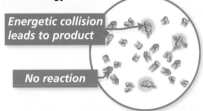

Energetic collision leads to product

No reaction

Factors Affecting the Rates of Chemical Reactions

The following factors affect the rate of chemical reactions:

Temperature	An increase in temperature increases the rate of reaction as the particles have more energy, move around quicker and collide more frequently.
Concentration of the Reactant	An increase in the concentration of the reactants in a solution increases the rate of reaction because there are more particles in a given volume. This means that the particles will collide more frequently.
Pressure of Reacting Gases	An increase in the pressure of reacting gases also means that there are more particles within a given volume and the particles will collide more frequently.
Surface Area of a Solid Reactant	Increasing the surface area of a solid (e.g. by making it into a powder) increases the rate of reaction because more particles are exposed to the other reactants, resulting in more collisions.
Presence of a Catalyst	A catalyst is a substance that increases the rate of a chemical reaction without itself undergoing any permanent chemical change. Catalysts work by providing a different pathway with a lower activation energy for the reaction. Because catalysts are not reactants, they are not included in the chemical equation for the reaction.

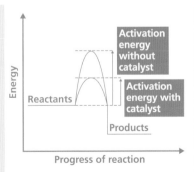

A decrease in these factors or the absence of a catalyst decreases the rate of reaction.

Reversible Reactions

The equation for a reversible reaction has a double arrow to show that the reaction can go in either direction.

Products
A + B
forwards ⇌ backwards
Reactants
C + D

The overall direction of reversible reactions can be changed by changing the conditions.

ammonium chloride ⇌ **ammonia + hydrogen chloride**

heat / cool

Ammonium chloride is broken down into ammonia and hydrogen chloride when it is heated.

Ammonia can react with hydrogen chlorine to reform ammonium chloride when cooled.

Energy Changes

If a reversible reaction is exothermic in one direction, it will be endothermic in the other. The same amount of energy will be transferred in each case.

In this reaction, there is an energy change of +78 kJ when the hydrated copper sulfate is heated to form anhydrous copper sulfate and water in an endothermic reaction.

hydrated copper sulfate ⇌ **anhydrous copper sulfate + water**

endothermic / exothermic

Conversely, there is an energy change of −78 kJ when the anhydrous copper sulfate is rehydrated with water in an exothermic reaction.

Equilibrium

In a closed system (from which reactants or products cannot escape), a reversible reaction will eventually reach equilibrium, where the forward and backward reactions are occurring at the same rate.

Reaching equilibrium does not mean that there is an equal amount (concentration) of products and reactants. Rather, it means that the amount of the respective reactants and products is constant.

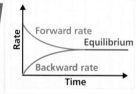

Equilibrium Position Left

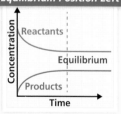

There are more reactants than products at equilibrium.

Equilibrium Position Centre

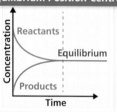

The amount of reactants and the products is the same.

Equilibrium Position Right

There are more products than reactants at equilibrium.

daydream EDUCATION

In some reactions, the products react with each other to reform the reactants. These are reversible reactions.

Le Chatelier's Principle

The relative amounts of reactants and products at equilibrium depend on the conditions of the reaction. Le Chatelier's principle states that if a system is at equilibrium and a change is made to its conditions, the system will respond to counteract the change.

Change in Temperature

In the case of an exothermic or endothermic reaction:

If there is a decrease in temperature, the equilibrium will shift in the exothermic direction to counteract this and raise the temperature.

If the forward reaction is exothermic and the backward reaction is endothermic, the equilibrium position shifts to the right, increasing the concentration of products and decreasing the concentration of reactants.

If there is an increase in temperature, the equilibrium will shift in the endothermic direction to counteract this and lower the temperature.

If the forward reaction is exothermic and the backward reaction is endothermic, the equilibrium position shifts to the left, decreasing the concentration of products and increasing the concentration of reactants.

Change in Concentration

When the concentration of a reactant or a product changes, the concentration of the substance will change until equilibrium is re-established.

Increase in Concentration

If there is an increase in reactant concentration, the equilibrium will shift towards the products to re-establish equilibrium. This will decrease the concentration of reactants and increase the concentration of products.

Decrease in Concentration

If there is a decrease in reactant concentration, the equilibrium will shift towards the reactants to re-establish equilibrium. This will increase the concentration of reactants and decrease the concentration of products.

Change in Pressure

Changing the pressure in a reverse reaction only affects gases.

An increase in pressure shifts the equilibrium towards the side with fewer molecules.

A decrease in pressure shifts the equilibrium towards the side with more molecules.

Crude Oil

Crude oil is a finite resource found in rocks. It is used as a raw material in many products, including solvents, fuels, detergents and plastics.

How Crude Oil Forms

Crude oil is a fossil fuel that has formed over millions of years from the remains of biomass (mainly plankton) that was buried in mud.

Organisms die and fall to the sea bed.

They get covered in layers of mud.

The mud turns into rock, and the organisms decay to form crude oil.

Crude oil is a mixture of many different compounds, most of which are hydrocarbons (molecules made of only hydrogen and carbon atoms).

Hydrocarbons exist as chains of different lengths and rings; all have a carbon atom backbone.

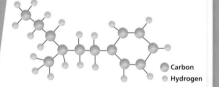

● Carbon
● Hydrogen

Alkanes

Most of the hydrocarbons in crude oil belong to the alkanes, a series of hydrocarbons that share the same general formula:

$$C_nH_{2n+2}$$

Methane (CH_4)

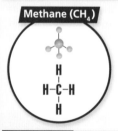

Ethane (C_2H_6)

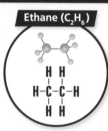

Propane (C_3H_8)

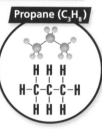

Butane (C_4H_{10})

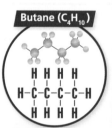

Formula

If you know the number of carbon or hydrogen atoms in an alkane, you can work out its formula.

The formula of an alkane with 10 carbon atoms is:

$$C_nH_{2n+2}$$
$$C_{10}H_{(2 \times 10)+2}$$
$$C_{10}H_{22}$$

daydream EDUCATION

Fractional Distillation

The molecules in crude oil have different lengths and, therefore, different boiling points. This means that they can be separated into mixtures with similar boiling points using fractional distillation.

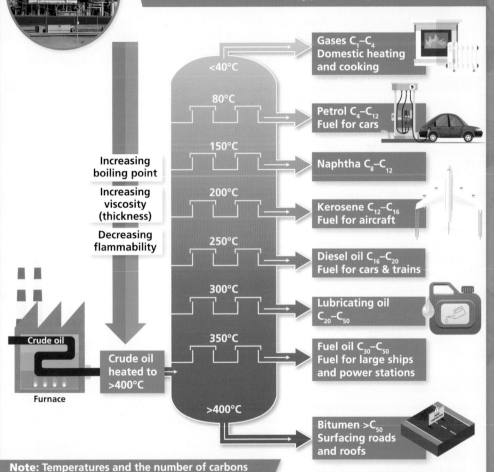

Increasing boiling point

Increasing viscosity (thickness)

Decreasing flammability

Crude oil

Furnace

Crude oil heated to >400°C

<40°C — Gases C_1–C_4 Domestic heating and cooking

80°C — Petrol C_4–C_{12} Fuel for cars

150°C — Naphtha C_8–C_{12}

200°C — Kerosene C_{12}–C_{16} Fuel for aircraft

250°C — Diesel oil C_{16}–C_{20} Fuel for cars & trains

300°C — Lubricating oil C_{20}–C_{50}

350°C — Fuel oil C_{30}–C_{50} Fuel for large ships and power stations

>400°C — Bitumen $>C_{50}$ Surfacing roads and roofs

Note: Temperatures and the number of carbons in hydrocarbons are approximates.

The fractionating column is cooler at the top and hotter at the bottom. Crude oil is heated so most of the molecules evaporate and turn into a gas. The gases travel up the column and progressively cool down, causing them to condense at different levels.

The resulting fractions can then be processed into fuels that are vital for modern life. The uses of the different fractions are shown on the diagram above.

Properties of Hydrocarbons

The ability of carbon atoms to bond together to form families of similar compounds means that there is a vast array of carbon compounds. Many of these are hydrocarbons, which contain only carbon and hydrogen. The properties of hydrocarbons are often related to the size of their molecules.

Boiling Point

As the molecules get larger, they become less volatile and their boiling point gets higher.

Flammability

Fuels need to vaporise to burn. The larger the hydrocarbon molecule, the more difficult it is to vaporise and so the less flammable it is.

Viscosity

Larger chains of molecules have more intermolecular forces and so are more viscous (i.e. less runny).

The properties of hydrocarbons influence how they are used.

Many hydrocarbons are used as fuels. The ones with smaller molecules make the best fuels because they are the most flammable. During combustion, the carbon and hydrogen in the fuel are oxidised (to produce carbon dioxide and water), and energy is released.

Combustion of methane

methane CH_4 + oxygen $2O_2$ $\longrightarrow$ carbon dioxide CO_2 + water $2H_2O$

Cracking

Short-chain hydrocarbons are flammable and useful as fuels. Therefore, long-chain hydrocarbons are often broken down into smaller molecules in a process called cracking. Cracking produces short alkanes plus alkenes. Alkenes contain double bonds and can be used to make polymers (plastics).

C_6H_{14}

Long alkane

Cracking $\longrightarrow$

C_4H_{10}

Shorter, more useful alkane

+

C_2H_4

Alkene

There are different methods of cracking, each of which produces a mix of different types of product.

- **Catalytic cracking** involves heating long-chain alkenes to vaporise them and then passing them over a catalyst (often silica-alumina) to speed up their breakdown.

- **Steam cracking** involves heating long-chain alkenes to vaporise them and mixing them with steam. The mixture is then heated to around 850°C for a few milliseconds in the absence of oxygen to breakdown the long-chain hydrocarbons into short alkanes and alkenes.

Testing for Alkenes

Alkenes can be distinguished from alkanes by their reaction with orange bromine water.

Alkanes do not react with bromine water, but alkenes are more reactive and remove the bromine, so the bromine water turns colourless.

Alkane   Alkene

daydream
EDUCATION

Purity & Formulations

Pure Substances

In everyday language, *pure* often refers to a substance that has had nothing else added to it, but the 'substance' in this case is not necessarily a single element or compound (e.g. 'pure' milk). In chemistry, a pure substance is a single element or compound that has not been mixed with any other substance.

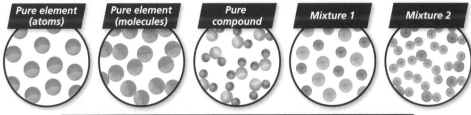

Pure element (atoms)   Pure element (molecules)   Pure compound   Mixture 1   Mixture 2

Pure elements and compounds have specific melting and boiling points.

If another substance is mixed in, the melting and boiling points will change. As a result, melting and boiling point data can be used to distinguish mixtures from pure substances. The purer the sample, the closer its melting and boiling points will be to those of the pure substance.

Example:

Methanol has a boiling point of 64.7°C. Three mixtures containing methanol are tested. Their boiling points are:

A 65.3°C   **B** 67.4°C   **C** 66.3°C

From this, we can determine that mixture A contains the least impurities because its boiling point is the nearest to that of pure methanol.

Formulations

A formulation is a mixture that has been designed as a useful substance.
Formulations are made by mixing components in carefully measured quantities.
This is necessary to ensure the formulation has the desired properties for its use.

Some common formulations:

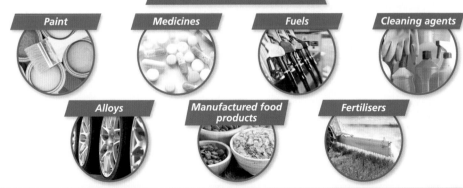

Paint   Medicines   Fuels   Cleaning agents

Alloys   Manufactured food products   Fertilisers

Chromatography

Chromatography is a method for separating mixtures and identifying their components. There are various types of chromatography.

Separating and Identifying Substances in a Mixture

During chromatography, substances travel in two 'phases'. In paper chromatography, the stationary phase is the paper, and the mobile phase is the solvent.

How long each substance spends in each phase varies depending on its attraction to the paper and the solvent.

Substances that have a stronger attraction to the paper spend longer in the paper (the stationary phase) and move more slowly, only travelling a short distance up the paper.

More soluble substances, which have a stronger attraction to the solvent, spend longer in the mobile phase and move more quickly, travelling further up the paper.

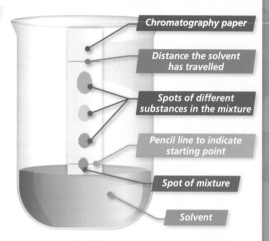

Chromatography paper

Distance the solvent has travelled

Spots of different substances in the mixture

Pencil line to indicate starting point

Spot of mixture

Solvent

In the example above, the blue substance has spent the longest time in the stationary phase, so it has moved the shortest distance. This means that it has a strong attraction to the paper.

Conversely, the green substance has spent the longest time in the mobile phase, so it has moved the farthest. This means that it has a strong attraction to the solvent.

R_f Values

The R_f value is the ratio of the distance moved by the dissolved substance to the distance moved by the solvent.

$$R_f = \frac{\text{distance travelled by substance}}{\text{distance travelled by solvent}}$$

Different compounds have different R_f values in a specific solvent. Therefore, the R_f can be used to identify the components (compounds) in a mixture.

Uses of Chromatography Recap

Separating Mixtures	Chromatography is used to separate mixtures. It is easiest to separate coloured mixtures, but methods are available that can identify transparent 'spots'.
Testing Purity	Compounds in a mixture may separate depending on the solvent, but a pure substance produces only one spot in all solvents.
Identifying Substances	It is possible to identify different compounds using their R_f value.

daydream
EDUCATION

Identification of Common Gases

Test for Hydrogen

A burning splint is held at the mouth of a test tube of the gas. Hydrogen burns rapidly with a characteristic 'squeaky pop'.

Test for Oxygen

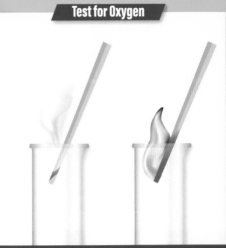

A glowing splint is inserted into the gas to be tested. If oxygen is present, the splint will re-light.

Test for Carbon Dioxide

The gas to be tested is shaken with or bubbled through limewater (calcium hydroxide). If carbon dioxide is present, the limewater will turn cloudy or milky due to the formation of insoluble calcium carbonate.

Test for Chlorine

Damp blue litmus paper is placed into the gas to be tested. Chlorine will briefly turn the paper red and then bleach it white.

The Earth's Atmosphere

Argon 0.9% | Other 0.1%

Oxygen 21%

Nitrogen 78%

The Proportion of Gases in the Atmosphere

The Earth's atmosphere is dynamic and constantly changing. However, the proportion of gases in the atmosphere has been roughly the same for the last 200 million years.

Nitrogen and oxygen make up approximately 99% of the Earth's atmosphere. Other gases include carbon dioxide, water vapour and noble gases.

The Early Atmosphere

The proportion of gases in the atmosphere was different when the Earth was first formed. Theories of what was in Earth's early atmosphere have changed over time, and evidence is limited because the Earth was formed over 4.6 billion years ago.

When the Earth formed, its first atmosphere would have been made of hydrogen and helium, but these low-density gases would have quickly drifted into space. The chart below shows one theory of how our atmosphere formed.

Stage	Events	Atmosphere
1	Intense volcanic activity produced gases and water vapour.	Carbon dioxide, water vapour, ammonia, methane and very little oxygen (similar to the current atmospheres of Mars and Venus)
2	The Earth continued to cool, and water vapour in the atmosphere condensed to form oceans. Carbon dioxide dissolved in the water, and carbonates were precipitated, producing sediments. Early plant life evolved.	Mostly carbon dioxide; some water vapour, nitrogen and ammonia
3	Early forms of plant life emerged, which used carbon dioxide to form oxygen through photosynthesis. Some of the oxygen reacted with ammonia to form nitrogen.	Current atmosphere, including nitrogen and oxygen

daydream EDUCATION

How Oxygen Increased

Oxygen started to be produced on Earth about 2.7 billion years ago, with the appearance of algae and plants, which carry out photosynthesis.

Photosynthesis is the process by which plants, algae and other organisms produce their own food (glucose). It uses light energy, carbon dioxide and water to produce glucose and oxygen. It can be represented by this equation:

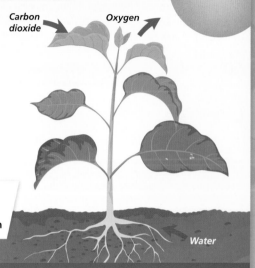

Carbon dioxide

Oxygen

Water

$$6CO_2 \ + \ 6H_2O \ \longrightarrow \ C_6H_{12}O_6 \ + \ 6O_2$$

carbon dioxide + water →(*light*) glucose + oxygen

Over the next billion years more plants evolved, and the percentage of oxygen in the atmosphere increased sufficiently to allow animal life to develop and evolve.

How Carbon Dioxide Decreased

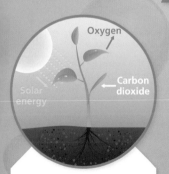

Oxygen

Solar energy

Carbon dioxide

The formation of oxygen by photosynthesis also leads to a decrease in the percentage of carbon dioxide in the atmosphere.

Carbon Dioxide (CO_2)

Sea

Sedimentary rock

Large amounts of carbon dioxide also dissolved in the oceans, forming sediments (precipitates) which gave rise to sedimentary rocks (e.g. limestone – calcium carbonate).

Sea

Mud layer → Rock layer

Dead organisms → Crude oil

Sea bed

The dead bodies of microscopic plants became compressed by this rock formation and were converted into fossil fuels – coal, oil and gas.

Atmospheric Pollution

The Earth's atmosphere has become polluted in a variety of ways by human activity.

Pollution from Fuels

Most fuels are carbon based, although many also contain hydrogen, sulfur and nitrogen compounds.

During the combustion of fuels, the compounds react with oxygen to become oxidised. As a result, several gases are released into the atmosphere.

Complete Combustion of Hydrocarbon Fuels

Carbon dioxide and water vapour are released by the complete combustion of hydrocarbon fuels.

hydrocarbon + oxygen carbon dioxide + water

Carbon dioxide and water vapour are greenhouse gases, which many people believe contribute to global warming and climate change.

Incomplete Combustion of Hydrocarbon Fuels

When there is not enough oxygen for complete combustion of hydrocarbon fuels, particles of carbon (soot) and carbon monoxide can also be released.

hydrocarbon + oxygen carbon dioxide + carbon monoxide + carbon + water

Carbon monoxide is a dangerous gas because it is highly toxic. It is also colourless and odourless, which makes it difficult to detect.

Carbon can also be released as small particles of unburnt hydrocarbons known as soot. These particles can cause health problems in humans and global dimming.

Health Problems

Particles of soot can be inhaled, causing respiratory problems, including coronary heart disease, asthma, bronchitis and cancer.

Global Dimming

Particles of soot in the atmosphere can block sunlight, reducing the amount of light reaching the surface of the Earth.

Sulfur Dioxide and Oxides of Nitrogen

Sulfur dioxide and nitrogen oxides also cause atmospheric pollution.

Sulfur dioxide is released due to sulfur impurities in many hydrocarbon fuels such as coal. Nitrogen oxides form at high temperatures when oxygen and nitrogen in the air react.

Both products can cause respiratory problems and acid rain. Acid rain is created when the products dissolve in water vapour in clouds to form sulfuric and nitric acids.

Greenhouse Gases

Greenhouse gases (including water vapour, carbon dioxide and methane) absorb infrared radiation from the Sun and keep the Earth warm enough to sustain life.

The Greenhouse Effect

The greenhouse effect is a naturally occurring phenomenon that insulates the Earth and keeps it warm enough to sustain life. However, it is believed that human activity increases the greenhouse effect, resulting in higher global temperatures.

a
When the Sun's solar radiation reaches the Earth's surface, most of it is absorbed, but some is reflected into the atmosphere.

b
The Earth absorbs radiation with short wavelengths and warms up. Heat is then radiated from the Earth as longer wavelength infrared radiation.

c
Some of this infrared radiation is absorbed by greenhouse gases in the atmosphere, and the atmosphere warms up.

The Effect of Human Activity on Greenhouse Gas Levels

A number of human activities are thought to play a role in the increase in the greenhouse gases methane and carbon dioxide in the atmosphere.

Fossil Fuels

Fossil fuels such as oil, gas and coal are burnt to generate energy for transportation, manufacturing and electricity production. However, the process of burning fossil fuels releases CO_2 into the atmosphere and is the main source of greenhouse gas emissions.

Agriculture

Agriculture, especially livestock and rice farming, produces huge amounts of the greenhouse gas methane. It is released by animals during digestion and by matter decomposed by microbes in flooded rice paddy fields.

Deforestation

Trees absorb CO_2 through photosynthesis. Therefore, clearing trees results in less CO_2 being removed from the atmosphere. This is worsened by the burning of fossil fuels, which also releases greenhouse gases into the atmosphere.

Based on peer-reviewed evidence, many scientists believe that human activities have caused, and will continue to cause, the temperature of the atmosphere to rise, resulting in global climate change. However, not everyone agrees with this theory.

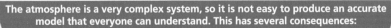

The atmosphere is a very complex system, so it is not easy to produce an accurate model that everyone can understand. This has several consequences:

Simplified models do not fully explain the theory and therefore may be misleading.

Speculation and media reports may only present parts of the evidence.

Some opinions may be biased (e.g. those from industries that produce greenhouse gases).

Effects of Climate Change

Climate change has a significant effect on both the environment and people.

Warmer global temperatures will cause glaciers and ice sheets to melt, leading to rising sea levels and the loss of polar habitats.

Rising sea levels will result in low-lying coastal areas flooding more frequently or even becoming permanently submerged in water.

Many plant and animal species are at risk of becoming extinct as their habitats are altered or damaged by climate change. For example, many of the world's coral reefs, which support a diverse range of marine life, are at risk of bleaching and destruction due to rising sea temperatures.

Warmer temperatures and higher sea levels will lead to more extreme weather events and a change in precipitation patterns.

Although agriculture in some areas may benefit from warmer temperatures, many areas will become hotter and drier. This will result in drought, desertification, declining crop yields and food and water shortages.

The Carbon Footprint

A carbon footprint is the total amount of carbon dioxide and other greenhouse gases emitted over the full life cycle of a product, service or event. Carbon footprints can be reduced by decreasing carbon dioxide and methane emissions. Examples include:

 Alternative Energy Production: This includes energy sources, such as hydroelectric power and solar power, which have lower greenhouse gas emissions than burning fossil fuels.

 Energy Conservation: Energy use and greenhouse gas emissions can be reduced by using energy-efficient devices and appliances.

 Recycling: Using recycled and recyclable materials can reduce the amount of fossil fuels required to create new materials.

 Reducing Deforestation & Planting Trees: The increase in greenhouse gas emissions from burning fossil fuels can be offset by reducing deforestation rates and planting trees, which absorb carbon dioxide.

 Carbon Capture & Storage: This involves capturing carbon dioxide released by industry or burning fossil fuels and then storing it safely underground.

There are some difficulties in reducing carbon footprints:

Many countries rely on fossil fuels for their economic prosperity, so it is against their interests to cease production and use.	*Alternative energy sources can be costly and do not produce as much energy as burning fossil fuels.*	*Measures may require lifestyle changes (e.g. recycling and reducing car use), which some people are unwilling to make.*

daydream
EDUCATION

The Earth's Resources

All resources essential for human development – from oxygen in the air we breathe to food, water, fuel, clothing and building materials – are all sourced from the Earth.

Earth's resources provide:

Warmth **Food** **Shelter** **Transport**

Non-Renewable Resources

These resources are finite and will eventually run out. Once they are depleted, they cannot be replenished.

Renewable Resources

These resources are infinite. They can be easily replenished and will not run out.

Sustainable development is development that meets the needs of the present without compromising the ability of future generations to meet their own needs.

The Six Rs of Sustainable Development

Rethink — Think before you buy or use products.

Refuse — Do not use products that are environmentally unsustainable.

Repair — Fix or repair items rather than throwing them away.

Reduce — Limit the amount of resources you use.

Reuse — Find new uses for old objects instead of throwing them away.

Recycle — Recycle what you can, and use recycled materials when possible.

Recycling Materials

Metal, glass, plastic and building materials are usually made from limited raw materials. To reduce the usage of these materials and to ensure that they last long, they can be reused or recycled.

 Although recycling can be expensive and require lots of energy, it generally requires less energy and generates less pollution than mining and extraction. It also reduces damage to the environment and landscape.

Metals

Metals can be recycled by melting them down and making them into something new. This means mining and the pollution caused by it are reduced, finite resources are conserved and there is less waste.

Glass

Glass can often be reused. Alternatively, if it is separated by colour and chemical composition, it can be crushed and melted to make new products.

The Role of Chemistry in Sustainable Development

Chemistry can improve agricultural and industrial processes and lead to new products that can aid sustainable development. Examples include:

- The use of catalysts to speed up chemical reactions so that they require less energy input

- The development and use of carbon nanotubes to strengthen materials and extend their life

- Researching conditions that make manufacturing processes more efficient

- Developing pesticides that break down and so do not enter food chains or pollute the environment

- Developing 'smart' materials that can be added to soil to retain water

daydream
EDUCATION

Potable Water

Water is essential for life. It is used for drinking, washing, sanitation, cooking, and industrial and manufacturing processes.

Potable water is water that is safe to drink. It is not pure water – it contains dissolved substances, including a safe level of dissolved salts and microbes. After use, waste water must be treated before being released back into the environment.

Local conditions and the availability of water supplies determine how potable water is produced.

UK Potable Water Supply

In the UK, water is sourced from rain that has gathered in groundwater stores, rivers, lakes and reservoirs. It has a low level of dissolved substances but still needs to be treated before it is safe to drink.

Treatment often consists of three stages:

1 The water is allowed to settle. Large soil particles settle to the bottom, and the water is drawn from the top.

2 The water is passed through filter beds, which filter out smaller particles.

3 The filtered water is then sterilised to remove most bacteria. The sterilising agents include chlorine, ozone and ultraviolet light.

Some countries do not have a sufficient supply of freshwater. Potable water can also be obtained from seawater by a process of desalination.

Desalination can be done by distillation or by processes that use membranes (e.g. reverse osmosis), but these processes require large amounts of energy and are expensive.

Heat the mixture until the substance with the lowest boiling point starts to boil and turn into a gas.

The gas cools, condenses in the condenser and collects in the beaker. The rest of the mixture remains in the flask.

Make sure you heat the solution to the boiling point of only one of the substances. If you heat the solution to a temperature at which both substances boil, they will become mixed again.

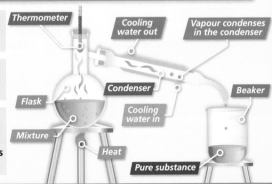

Thermometer
Cooling water out
Vapour condenses in the condenser
Condenser
Beaker
Flask
Cooling water in
Mixture
Heat
Pure substance

daydream EDUCATION

Waste Water Treatment

After use, waste water must be treated before being released back into the environment. Potable water is a limited resource so it must be recycled for reuse where possible. Waste water comes from several sources.

Domestic Use	Water is used in the home for cleaning, washing and flushing away wastes. Sewage needs to be treated to remove harmful bacteria and organic matter.
Agriculture	Water is used in agriculture for irrigation (watering crops). Waste water, which often contains pesticides and fertilisers, drains into streams and rivers.
Industry	Most water extracted from freshwater sources is used for energy production. It is also used for manufacturing. Waste water from industry needs to be treated to remove organic matter and harmful chemicals including oil.

Sewage Treatment

Sewage treatment cleans waste water to make it fit for drinking.

1 Screening
Large sediment and grit is removed, and the sewage is passed to a sedimentation tank.

2 Sedimentation
The sewage is left to settle so heavy sediment sinks to the bottom and lighter effluent floats to the top.

3 Aerobic Treatment
The effluent is drained into an aeration tank where it is pumped with air. Good bacteria breaks down harmful bacteria through aerobic digestion.

4 Release
The treated water is released back into the environment.

During anaerobic digestion, the bacteria produce methane, which can be burned and used as an energy source.

The heavy sediment (sludge) is moved to a separate tank where it is broken down anaerobically by bacteria.

The digested waste can be used as fertiliser.

daydream EDUCATION

Alternative Methods of Metal Extraction

Most metals are found in rocks called ores and have to be extracted from these ores through mining. Due to their over-extraction, the Earth's resources of metal ores are diminishing.

Some metals, such as copper, have become so scarce that low-grade ores, which contain a small percentage of copper, are having to be mined through new methods of extraction.

Phytomining

Phytomining is used to extract copper from soil that is rich in copper compounds.

2 Plants containing copper are burnt.

3 Copper is extracted from the ash.

1 Plants absorb copper ions from the soil.

Bioleaching

Bioleaching uses bacteria that absorb copper compounds to produce solutions called leachates, which contain copper compounds.

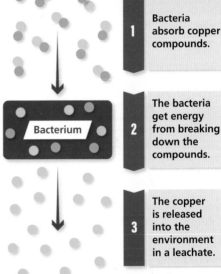

Bacterium

1 Bacteria absorb copper compounds.

2 The bacteria get energy from breaking down the compounds.

3 The copper is released into the environment in a leachate.

After phytomining and bioleaching, the copper can be extracted from the ash or the leachate. Extraction is done through a **displacement** reaction using scrap iron (because iron is more reactive than copper) or by **electrolysis**.

Environmental Benefits

Neither phytomining nor bioleaching involves traditional mining practices such as digging or moving and disposing of large amounts of rock. Therefore, they are better for the environment.

Life Cycle Assessment

Life cycle assessments (LCAs) are used to assess the environmental impacts of every stage of a product's life (including disposal).

1 Extraction & Processing

- Does extraction and processing damage the environment and cause pollution?
- Does extracting the material require large amounts of energy and create lots of waste?

2 Manufacturing & Packaging

- Does the manufacturing process use large amounts of energy, cause pollution or produce harmful waste products?
- Does the packaging create a lot of waste?
- Can the packaging be recycled?

3 Use & Operation

- Does the product damage the environment?
- Does the product require lots of energy to run?
- How long is the product's lifecycle?

4 Product Disposal

- How easy is it to dispose of the product?
- Does the process of disposal result in pollution?
- Can it be reused or recycled after use?
- Is the product biodegradable?

Evaluating the Sustainability of Using Paper and Plastic Bags

Paper Bags	LCA Stage	Plastic Bags
Made from sustainable trees, but require large amounts of energy to produce	Extraction and Processing	Made from crude oil, which is a finite resource
Total energy use: 2,622 MJ Freshwater usage: 1,004 gal	Manufacturing and Packaging (figures based on 1,000 bags)	Total energy use: 763 MJ Freshwater usage: 58 gal
Not very strong and do not last very long Not waterproof	Use and Operation	Can be reused as a bag and for other purposes, such as bin liners
Biodegradable and can be recycled	Product Disposal	Not biodegradable but can be recycled Often end up in landfill

Each type of bag has benefits and drawbacks, so a judgement must be made on which benefits are most important. It is not always possible or easy to quantify figures in an LCA. Figures are often biased because they are based on value judgements.

Sometimes LCAs can be misused. Selective or shortened LCAs can be presented (e.g. in advertising) so as to reach predetermined and preferred conclusions.

daydream EDUCATION

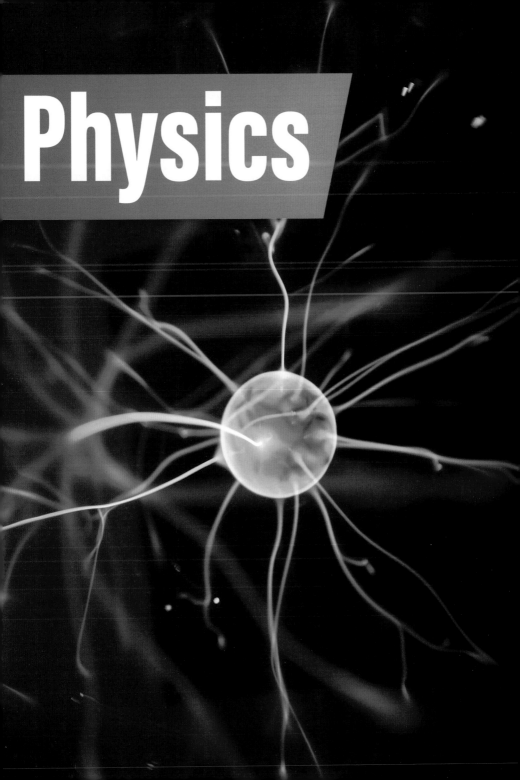

Physics

Energy Stores & Systems

Energy Stores

Energy cannot be created or destroyed. It can only be transferred or transformed from one energy store to another. Energy is measured in joules (J). There are many different energy stores, including:

 M Magnetic
 G Gravitational potential
 **E** Electrostatic
 T Thermal
 N Nuclear
 E Elastic potential
 C Chemical
 K Kinetic

Light, sound and electricity are NOT stores of energy.
They are ways of transferring energy from one store to another.

Energy Transfer

Energy is stored in different systems (an object or group of objects), and when a system changes, energy can be transferred by:

Heating   **Work done by forces**   **Work done when a current flows**   **Radiation**

Examples of Energy Transfer in Systems

1 When an electric kettle is switched on, the water gets hotter. There is now more **thermal energy** (or **internal energy**) stored in the hot water than there was when it was cold. Energy has been transferred by electricity (**work done when a current flows**) and **heating**.

2 When a moving object hits an obstacle, some of its store of **kinetic energy** is transferred into different energy stores in the obstacle. If the obstacle breaks, each broken piece will carry some of the **kinetic energy** away. If the obstacle does not break, then some of the kinetic energy from the object will likely be transferred into **thermal energy** in the object and the obstacle.

3 When someone throws a ball, **chemical energy** in the person's arm is transferred to the **kinetic energy** store of the ball and the arm. Energy has been transferred mechanically by **work done by forces**.

4 When a vehicle brakes, the **kinetic energy** store in the car wheel is transferred to the **thermal energy** store of the brakes. Energy has been transferred by **work done against the force of friction**. For example, Formula One cars brake at such high speeds that they must be specifically designed to withstand high temperatures.

daydream EDUCATION

Calculating Energy Stores

The amount of energy in some of the most common energy stores can be calculated using the following formulae.

Kinetic Energy Stores

A moving object has a store of kinetic energy. When an object speeds up, energy is transferred into the store; when it slows down, energy is transferred out. The greater the mass and speed of the object, the greater its store of kinetic energy.

joules (J)   kilograms (kg)

kinetic energy = 0.5 × mass × (speed)²

$$[E_k = \frac{1}{2}m\,v^2]$$

metres per second (m/s)

A car is travelling at a speed of 30 m/s and has a mass of 1,200 kg. Calculate the kinetic energy of the car.

Kinetic energy = 0.5 × mass × (speed)²
= 0.5 × 1,200 × (30)²
= 0.5 × 1,200 × 900
= 540,000 J or 540 kJ

Gravitational Potential Energy (GPE) Stores

An object raised above ground level has a store of GPE. The greater the strength of the gravitational field and the height and mass of the object, the greater its store of GPE. The gravitational field at the Earth's surface produces a force of approximately 9.8 N/kg. This means that an object with a mass of 1 kg is attracted towards the centre of the Earth by a force of 9.8 N.

joules (J)   kilograms (kg)   metres (m)

GPE = mass × gravitational field strength × height

$$[E_p = m\,g\,h]$$

newtons per kilogram (N/kg)

A crane raises a crate to a height of 15 m. It has gained 22,500 J of GPE. Calculate the mass of the crate.

GPE = mass × gravitational field strength × height

$$mass = \frac{GPE}{gravitational\ field\ strength \times height}$$

$$= \frac{22,500}{9.8 \times 15}$$

= 153 kg (3 s.f.)

Rearrange the equation to make mass the subject.

Elastic Potential Energy Stores

A squashed or stretched object has a store of elastic potential energy. The more an object is stretched or squashed, the greater its store of elastic potential energy – as long as the object has not exceeded its limit of proportionality.

joules (J)   newtons per metre (N/m)

elastic potential energy = 0.5 × spring constant × (extension)²

$$[E_e = \frac{1}{2}k\,e^2]$$

metres (m)

A spring with a spring constant of 50 N/m is extended by 8 cm. Calculate the elastic potential energy stored in the spring.

elastic potential energy = 0.5 × spring constant × (extension)²
= 0.5 × 50 × (0.08)²
= 0.16 J

8 cm = 0.08 m

Work Done & Power

Force, Work Done and Power

A force is a push or pull that acts on an object. Work is done when a force acts on an object causing the object to move a distance in the direction of the force.

Work done can be calculated using the following equation:

joules (J)   newtons (N)   metres (m)

work = force × distance moved in the direction of the force

$[W = F s]$

Power is defined as the rate at which work is done on an object or the rate at which energy is transferred from one energy store to one or more energy stores.

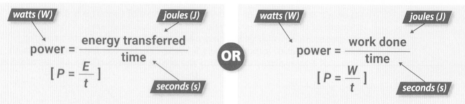

watts (W)   joules (J)

$$power = \frac{energy\ transferred}{time}$$

$[P = \frac{E}{t}]$

seconds (s)

OR

watts (W)   joules (J)

$$power = \frac{work\ done}{time}$$

$[P = \frac{W}{t}]$

seconds (s)

An energy transfer of 1 joule per second is equal to 1 watt of power.

Example

If one crane can lift a container more quickly than another crane lifting the same object, we say it is more powerful because it is transferring energy (or doing work) more quickly.

It takes 9000 J of work to lift a crate to the top of a tower. Motor A can lift the crate into place in 50 s. Motor B can do the same job in 60 s. Calculate the power of the two motors.

Motor A

$$power\ of\ motor\ A = \frac{work\ done}{time}$$

$$= \frac{9000}{50}$$

$$= 180\ W$$

Motor B

$$power\ of\ motor\ B = \frac{work\ done}{time}$$

$$= \frac{9000}{60}$$

$$= 150\ W$$

Motor A has transferred the same amount of energy as motor B, but it has done it in less time. The energy is now stored as gravitational potential energy.

daydream
EDUCATION

Energy Transfer and Efficiency

Energy can be transferred from one store to another, but it cannot be destroyed or created.

Energy Transfer

When there are energy transfers in a closed system, there is no net change in the total energy. However, some of the energy is dissipated or 'wasted', and is stored in less useful ways.

A **Sankey diagram** is often used to display the transfer of input energy into its useful and wasted outputs. It is drawn to scale, and the width of each arrow shows the amounts of energy involved.

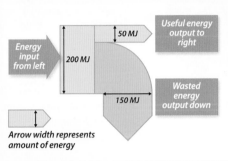

Energy input from left — 200 MJ
Useful energy output to right — 50 MJ
Wasted energy output down — 150 MJ
Arrow width represents amount of energy

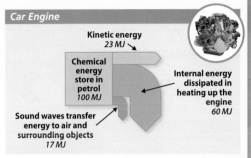

Car Engine

Kinetic energy 23 MJ
Chemical energy store in petrol 100 MJ
Internal energy dissipated in heating up the engine 60 MJ
Sound waves transfer energy to air and surrounding objects 17 MJ

Conservation of Energy

As you can see from the above Sankey diagrams, a lot of energy is dissipated. However, there are several ways of reducing unwanted energy transfers.

Lubrication and Aerodynamics

Moving objects have frictional forces acting upon them. These forces transfer a system's energy from its kinetic energy store to its internal/thermal energy store.

Making an object more aerodynamic reduces the air resistance acting upon it and, therefore, the amount of wasted energy. Travelling more slowly also reduces air resistance.

Additionally, objects that rub together create frictional forces that result in wasted internal / thermal energy. Lubricants, such as oil, can be used to reduce friction.

Insulation

The higher the thermal conductivity of a material, the higher the rate of energy transfer by conduction through the material. Because of this, new houses are often built with thick walls made of materials with a low thermal conductivity to reduce heat loss.

Thermal insulation is also used to reduce the movement of particles away from hotter areas to cooler areas by convection currents. Walls are built with an air gap between them to reduce energy loss.

The use of loft insulation, double-glazed windows and draught excluders also reduces heat loss through convection.

Efficiency

Efficiency is a measure of the proportion of the total input energy, work or power that is turned into useful output. The less energy dissipated from a system, the more efficient it is.

$$\text{efficiency} = \frac{\text{useful output}}{\text{total input}}$$

OR

$$\text{efficiency} = \frac{\text{useful output energy transfer}}{\text{total input energy transfer}}$$

A solar cell can usefully convert 4 J of input energy into 0.6 J of output energy every second.

Therefore, the efficiency of the solar cell is 0.15 or 15%.

$$\text{efficiency} = \frac{\text{useful output}}{\text{total input}}$$
$$= \frac{0.6}{4}$$
$$= 0.15$$

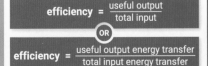

Energy Resources

Sources of energy, or energy resources, are used for generating electricity and for transport, heating and cooking. Each energy resource has different benefits and drawbacks.

Non-Renewable Resources

These resources are finite and will eventually run out. Once they are depleted, they cannot be replenished.

FOSSIL FUELS

 Coal Natural gas Crude oil

Nuclear

Renewable Resources

These resources are infinite. They can be easily replenished and will not run out.

 Solar (Sun) Wind

Geothermal Biofuels

Hydroelectric Tidal & wave

Changing Demand for Fuel in the UK

Traditionally, the UK's energy mix has consisted mainly of the fossil fuels coal, gas and oil. However, fossil fuel reserves are declining, and efforts are being made to reduce greenhouse gas emissions. As such, a big shift from fossil fuels to renewable energy sources is occurring.

The EU aims to have 32% of its energy mix made up of renewable energy by 2030.

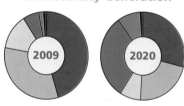

UK Electricity Generation

2009

2020

Gas Renewables Nuclear Coal Other Oil

How Different Energy Resources Are Used

Transport

Transport is one of the biggest contributors to greenhouse gas emissions in the UK, with oil-based fuels such as petrol, diesel and kerosene being the most popular fuels for transport.

Alternative renewable energy resources include biofuels and electrically-powered vehicles (if recharged using electricity from renewable power stations).

Most of the energy used in domestic heating comes from natural gas. However, electric heaters and wood, coal and heating oil burners are also used.

Heating

Energy consumption from heating can be reduced through improved efficiency – for example improved insulation, underfloor heating and the use of smart meters.

daydream EDUCATION

The UK's electricity supply comes from a wide variety of sources, with over 60% being generated from fossil fuels (mainly gas and coal). Nuclear power and renewable energy resources (mainly wind and biomass) make up most of the remaining 40%.

Fossil Fuels

The burning of fossil fuels releases CO_2 into the atmosphere and is the main source of greenhouse gas emissions. It is believed that the increase in greenhouse gases in the atmosphere has contributed to global warming, which has a significant effect on the environment and people.

Warmer global temperatures will cause glaciers and ice sheets to melt, leading to rising sea levels and the loss of polar habitats.

Rising sea levels will result in low-lying coastal areas flooding more frequently or even becoming permanently submerged in water.

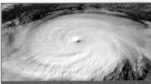

Warmer temperatures and higher sea levels will lead to more extreme weather and a change in precipitation patterns.

Other products of fossil fuel combustion include carbon monoxide, sulfur dioxide, soot and nitrogen oxide. These also affect human health and the environment, causing acid rain, smog and global dimming.

Alternative Energy Resources

To reduce dependence on fossil fuels, governments are looking to increase the use of alternative energy resources that are renewable and cause less damage to the environment.

Renewable energy sources are a good option for increasing the energy supply because they do not run out. However, each source has its associated advantages and disadvantages.

	Use	Advantage	Disadvantage
Biomass 	Organic materials, such as animal waste, wood and crops, are burned for energy or processed into biofuel.	Biomass is affordable and renewable if resources are replaced (e.g. trees are replanted).	Burning biomass releases CO_2. Using wood for fuel can lead to deforestation.
Wind	The generators in wind turbines use the kinetic energy store in the wind to produce electricity.	Wind power produces no greenhouse gases. Once turbines have been set up, wind is a cheap source of energy.	Set-up costs are high. Some people consider turbines an eyesore, and they also create noise pollution.

Hydroelectric Power (HEP)

Dams are used to trap and control water. As water is released, its kinetic energy store is used to turn turbines which are connected to electric generators.

Once infrastructure has been set up, HEP produces energy cheaply. Reservoirs provide a water supply during shortages.

Set-up costs are high. Also, when dams are built, habitats are often destroyed and people displaced.

Tidal

Currents and changes in tidal water levels are used to turn turbines and produce electricity.

Tides are guaranteed and predictable, and they produce no greenhouse gases.

Tidal barrages are costly to build and can disrupt ecosystems.

Geothermal

Heat from within the Earth is used to generate electricity.

Geothermal energy is a cheap energy source.

Power can only be harnessed from tectonically active areas.

Wave

Electricity is generated when waves turn turbines in the sea.

Wave power produces no greenhouse gases. It is well-suited to coastal areas.

It is costly to set up and produces little energy when the sea is calm.

Solar

Solar panels are used to convert the Sun's energy into electricity.

Once solar panels have been set up, solar energy is cheap. It produces no greenhouse gases.

No electricity is generated when there is no sunlight. Panels are expensive.

In addition to efforts to use more renewable energy resources, existing energy generation can be made more efficient.

Fossil Fuels

Power stations can reuse wasted heat or burn biomass as they generate electricity. New technologies can also be used to exploit resources that were once too difficult to extract – for example, fracking for shale gas.

Nuclear Power

Nuclear power stations can generate a lot of electricity without producing polluting gases. Used uranium rods can also be reused to improve efficiency. However, nuclear waste is highly dangerous, and any accidents from nuclear plants could be disastrous.

Reliability of Energy Resources

Few renewable energy resources are competitive with fossil fuels for cost, energy generation and reliability. However, fossil fuels are non-renewable and will eventually run out. Therefore, countries need to consider investing in alternative methods of energy production to ensure the long-term provision of energy.

146

daydream EDUCATION

The National Grid

Electrical power is generated by power stations. This is then transferred across the country through the National Grid.

Power station

Consumers

Step-up transformers

Pylons

Step-down transformers

 Step-up transformers are used to increase the potential difference from the power station to the cables that form the network across the UK.

 Step-down transformers are used to decrease the potential difference to a much lower value (230 V) for use in our homes.

A step-up transformer increases the potential difference but reduces the current in the cables of the National Grid. This reduces the energy dissipated (or lost) through heating of the cables.

The potential difference can be as large as 400,000 V (400 kV), which is very dangerous, so pylons are used to keep the cables a safe distance away from people.

daydream
EDUCATION

Circuit Symbols

Electrical circuit diagrams can sometimes look confusing. Here is an explanation of the most commonly used symbols.

Commonly Used Symbols

Cell	A cell is a store of chemical energy.		
Switch	A switch can be turned on (closed) to let current flow or turned off (open) to stop current flow.		
Motor	A motor turns current into motion, for example, in a hair dryer.		
Resistor	A fixed resistor controls the amount of current in a circuit.		
Voltmeter	A voltmeter is used to measure the potential difference between two points in an electrical circuit.		
Fuse	A fuse helps protect electrical circuits. It is usually a thin wire that melts and causes the circuit to break if too large a current flows through it.		
LDR	A light-dependent resistor (LDR) adapts to the amount of light it receives. As light intensity increases, resistance decreases.		

daydream
EDUCATION

Battery

A battery is two or more cells connected in series.

Diode

A diode allows current to flow in one direction only. It is normally used to prevent damage to other components.

LED

A light-emitting diode (LED) emits light when current flows the correct way through it.

Variable Resistor

A variable resistor can be adjusted to control the amount of current in a circuit.

Ammeter

An ammeter is used to measure current.

Bulb/Lamp

A bulb or lamp lights up only when it is in a circuit that is complete.

Thermistor

A thermistor is a type of resistor. Its resistance varies significantly with temperature.

Electrical Current, Potential Difference & Resistance

Electrical Charge and Current

Current is the flow of electrical charge. It is measured in amperes (**A**), or amps, using an ammeter. The measurement is the same at any point in a single closed-circuit loop. The size of the current is the rate of flow of electrical charge.

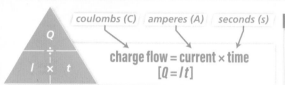

coulombs (C)   amperes (A)   seconds (s)

charge flow = current × time
$$[Q = It]$$

The charge that passes a point in a circuit is 1 coulomb when there is a current of 1 amp for 1 second.

Example

The current in a series circuit is 3.0 A. How much charge flows though the circuit in 5 minutes?

$Q = It$
$Q = 3.0 \times (5 \times 60)$
$Q = 3.0 \times 300$
$Q = 900 \, C$

Current, Potential Difference and Resistance

Potential Difference

For an electrical charge to flow through a closed circuit, there must be a potential difference to 'push' the charge around. Potential difference is measured in volts (V) using a voltmeter.

For a fixed resistance, the bigger the potential difference, the greater the current.

Resistance

Some components require a large potential difference to produce a current through them. This is because they have a high resistance (opposition to the flow of electrical charge). Resistance is measured in ohms (Ω).

For a fixed potential difference, the greater the resistance of a component, the smaller the current.

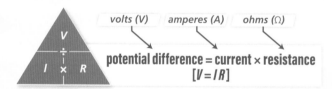

volts (V)   amperes (A)   ohms (Ω)

potential difference = current × resistance
$$[V = IR]$$

Example

The potential difference across the lamp is 9 V, and the current is 0.3 A.

Calculate the resistance of the lamp in this circuit.

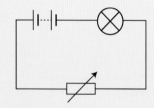

$R = \dfrac{V}{I}$

$R = \dfrac{9}{0.3}$

$R = 30 \, \Omega$

daydream
EDUCATION

Practical Activity: Investigate how the length of a wire at a constant temperature affects the resistance of electrical circuits.

There are various factors that affect the resistance of electrical circuits. The following practical activity can be used to determine how the length of a wire at a constant temperature affects the resistance.

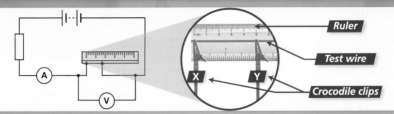

Ruler

Test wire

Crocodile clips

1 Set up the circuit as shown so you can measure the potential difference across and current through a test wire at different lengths. The voltmeter must be in parallel across the test wire.

2 Using a crocodile clip (X), connect the lead from the negative side of the ammeter to the test wire at zero on the ruler.

3 The lead from the negative side of the battery is then connected to the test wire at set intervals (e.g. every 5 cm) using another crocodile clip (Y). This lead is used as a switch for the battery between readings.

4 Create a table like the one below to record the results.

Length of wire (cm)	Potential Difference (V)	Current (A)	Resistance (Ω)
5			
10			
...			

5 Connect crocodile clip Y at the first distance, and measure the readings on the voltmeter and ammeter. Record the measurements in the table.

6 Disconnect crocodile clip Y and repeat step 5 for all intervals - 10 cm, 15 cm and so on.

7 Calculate the resistance for each length of wire using the following equation:

$$\text{resistance } (\Omega) = \frac{\text{potential difference (V)}}{\text{current (A)}}$$

8 Plot a graph of resistance against wire length. The resistance of the wire is directly proportional to its length so the graph should be a straight line through the origin.

There is a good chance that your graph may not pass through the origin. It is difficult to measure the length of the wire at 0 cm accurately, and there will be some contact resistance between the wire and the crocodile clips.

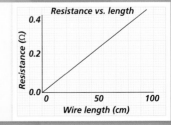

Resistance

The current through a component in a circuit is not always proportional to the potential difference across it. The resistance may change as the current changes.

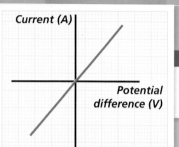

Ohmic Conductor (at a Constant Temperature)

The current through an ohmic conductor is directly proportional to the potential difference across it. Resistance remains constant as the current changes.

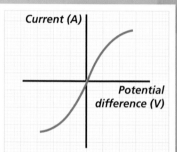

Filament Lamp

Resistance increases with temperature. Therefore, as current passes through the filament, the filament heats up, and resistance increases.

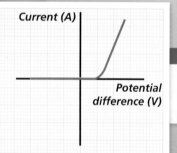

Diode

The current through a diode flows in one direction only. The diode has a very high resistance in the reverse direction and a very low resistance in the forward direction.

The resistance of some components changes in response to a change in their environment.

Thermistors

The resistance of a thermistor decreases as the temperature increases and vice versa. As a result, they are used in many applications such as fire alarms, air-conditioning units and fridges as a thermostat (temperature sensor).

LDRs

The resistance of an LDR decreases as light intensity increases and vice versa. As a result, they are used in many applications that require lights to be switched on when it gets dark, such as night lights and outdoor lighting.

daydream
EDUCATION

The following practical activity can be used to investigate the
I-V characteristics of resistors, filament lamps and diodes.

1 Set up the circuit as shown opposite.

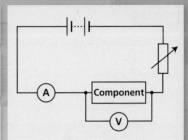

2 Connect a resistor to the circuit (where it says component) and set the variable resistor to a suitable value.

3 Record the readings on the ammeter and voltmeter in a suitable table.

4 Adjust the variable resistor to a new value, and record the new readings.

5 Repeat step 4, changing the resistance of the variable resistor, to obtain several pairs of readings.

6 Swap the connections on the battery so the direction of current is reversed, and record the readings on the ammeter and voltmeter. The readings should now be negative.

7 As before, adjust the variable resistor several times, and record the pairs of readings of current and potential difference.

8 Plot a graph of current against potential difference. It should look like the ohmic conductor graph in the Resistance section.

9 Replace the resistor with a filament lamp and repeat steps 1–8. The resulting graph should look like the filament lamp graph in the Resistance section.

10 To investigate the I-V characteristics of a diode, you will need to set up the circuit slightly differently, as shown opposite.

Reduce the battery pd to less than 5 V, connect an extra resistor (P) and replace the ammeter with a milliammeter (mA).

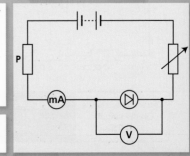

11 Repeat step 3–8. The resulting graph should look like the diode graph in the Resistance section.

Series & Parallel Circuits

Parallel Circuit

In a parallel circuit, components are placed on separate branches and each branch can be switched on and off independently. Also, if a component in one branch fails, the components in other branches will continue to work.

Series Circuit

In a series circuit, all components are connected in a single closed-circuit loop. Therefore, if one component breaks, all other components will fail.

Circuit A

V — 9 V
0.36 A → A
V₁   V₂
10 Ω   15 Ω

Circuit B

V — 2 V
0.2 A → A
Branch 1 → Lamp A
Branch 2 → Lamp B

Current

The current (I) through each of the components is the same: $I_1 = I_2 = I_3$ ... The current through all components in circuit A is 0.36 A.

current = potential difference ÷ resistance
= 9 ÷ (10 + 15)
= 9 ÷ 25
= 0.36 A

The total current through a circuit is the sum of the current through each branch. The current splits between each branch and then recombines.

If two components of the same resistance are connected in parallel, the same current will flow through them. For example, the current through lamps A and B is 0.1 A.

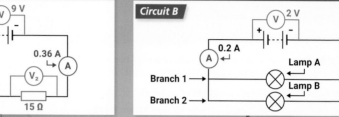

Potential Difference

The total potential difference (voltage) of the power supply is shared between the components according to their resistance.

potential difference = current × resistance	
V₁ = 0.36 × 10 = 3.6 V	V₂ = 0.36 × 15 = 5.4 V

The potential difference across each branch is the same. In circuit B, the potential difference across both lamps is 2 V.

If an additional lamp were added to branch 2, in series with lamp B, the potential difference of 2 V would be shared between the two lamps, and 1 V would go to each.

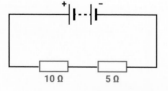

Resistance

The total resistance of two components in a series circuit, is the sum of their resistances:
$R_{total} = R_1 + R_2 + R_3$ ...

10 Ω   5 Ω

The total resistance in the circuit is **15 Ω**.	$R_{total} = R_1 + R_2$ = 10 + 5 = 15 Ω

The current in a parallel circuit can take multiple paths. Therefore, the resistance of the whole circuit is less than the resistance of any of the individual resistors.

$$\frac{1}{R_{total}} = \frac{1}{R_1} + \frac{1}{R_2} \text{ ...}$$

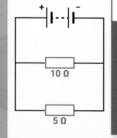

10 Ω

5 Ω

The total resistance in the circuit is **3.3 Ω**.

$$\frac{1}{R_{total}} = \frac{1}{10} + \frac{1}{5}$$
$$\frac{1}{R_{total}} = 0.1 + 0.2$$
$$\frac{1}{R_{total}} = 0.3$$
$$R_{total} = \frac{1}{0.3}$$
$$= 3.3 \, Ω$$

daydream
EDUCATION

Electric current can only flow if there is a complete circuit. There are two ways of joining electrical components: in series and in parallel. Some circuits include both series and parallel parts.

Investigating Resistance in Series and Parallel Circuits

The following investigation can be used to determine how the arrangement of resistors in series and in parallel affects resistance.

1 Set up the series circuit as shown opposite. The meters should be positioned as shown.

2 Switch on the circuit and record the voltage, or potential difference, across the resistor and the current through it.

3 Calculate the value of the resistor R_1:

$$\text{resistance} = \frac{\text{potential difference}}{\text{current}} \text{ or } R = \frac{V}{I}$$

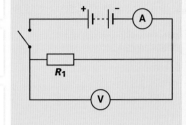

4 Take out resistor R_1, replace it with a different resistor (R_2), and repeat steps 2–3 to ensure R_1 and R_2 have the same value of resistance.

5 Set up the series circuit as shown opposite. Use wire wound resistors because they are less likely to overheat (and cause anomalous results).

6 Switch on the circuit, and record the readings of the ammeter and the voltmeter.

7 Calculate the total resistance of the circuit: $R = \frac{V}{I}$

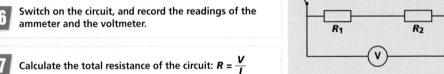

8 Set up the parallel circuit as shown, using the same resistors (R_1 and R_2) that were used in the series circuit.

9 Switch on the circuit, and record the readings of the ammeter and the voltmeter.

10 Calculate the total resistance of the circuit: $R = \frac{V}{I}$

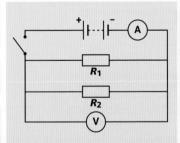

By performing this investigation, you should be able to reach the following conclusions:

As more resistors are added in series, the total resistance of the circuit will increase. The total resistance of the two resistors R_1 and R_2 is $R_1 + R_2$.

Conversely, as more resistors are added in parallel, the total resistance of the circuit will decrease. The total resistance of two resistors in parallel is less than the resistance of each individual resistor.

Electricity in the Home

Direct and Alternating Potential Difference

Electrical supplies can be direct current (dc) or alternating current (ac).

Direct Current (dc)

Potential Difference (V)

Time

In a direct current (dc) circuit, the battery or power supply provides a direct potential difference. This causes current to flow in one direction only, from the + to the – of the battery or power supply.

Alternating Current (ac)

Potential Difference (V)

Time

In an alternating power supply, the potential difference is constantly changing direction. This causes the current to go one way around the circuit and then the other, repeatedly.

Mains electricity is an alternating (ac) supply. In the UK, the domestic electricity supply has a frequency of 50 Hz and is about 230 V. The current alternates (goes one way then the other) 50 times per second.

Mains Electricity

In the home, most electrical appliances are connected to the mains supply by a three-pin plug at the end of a three-core cable.

The insulation around each wire is colour coded.

Live Wire (Brown)

The brown live wire carries the alternating potential difference from the plug socket to the appliance.

Neutral Wire (Blue)

The blue neutral wire completes the circuit. The live and neutral wires carry current to and from the appliance.

Earth Wire (Green and Yellow Stripes)

The green-and-yellow striped earth wire is a safety wire. There is a current in this wire only when the appliance circuit has developed a fault.

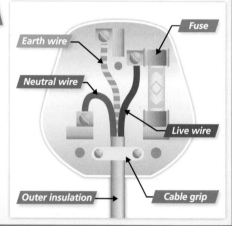

Earth wire

Fuse

Neutral wire

Live wire

Outer insulation

Cable grip

The earth wire is at a potential of 0 V. The potential difference between the live and earth wires is about 230 V. The neutral wire is very close to earth potential (0 V). The live wire can be dangerous even when the circuit is switched off. The fuse in the three pin plug helps reduce this danger by creating a gap (break) in the live part of the circuit when it fuses, melts or blows.

daydream
EDUCATION

Energy Transfers in Electrical Appliances

Energy Transfer

Everyday electrical appliances transfer chemical energy from batteries or ac mains to other energy stores by electricity. Work is done to move a charge round the circuit.

In an electric motor, energy is transferred from the chemical energy store in the battery to the kinetic energy store in the motor.

In a kettle, energy is transferred from the energy store in the ac mains to the thermal energy store of the heating element in the kettle.

Battery
Chemical energy store
→ *Electric current* →
Motor
Kinetic energy store

ac mains
Energy store
→ *Electric current* →
Kettle
Thermal energy store

Remember that not all energy is transferred usefully – some is dissipated, or wasted.

The amount of energy transferred by an appliance depends on how long the appliance has been switched on and the power of the appliance.

$\dfrac{E}{P \times t}$

joules (J)   watts (W)   seconds (s)

energy transferred = power × time
$$[E = Pt]$$

A kettle has a power rating of 2.2 kW and takes 2 minutes and 30 seconds to boil the water inside it. Calculate the energy transferred to the water.

$E = Pt$
$= 2,200 \times (2.5 \times 60)$
$= 330,000$ J or 330 kJ

The energy transferred can also be calculated using the following equation:

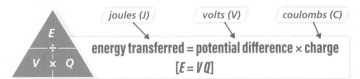

$\dfrac{E}{V \times Q}$

joules (J)   volts (V)   coulombs (C)

energy transferred = potential difference × charge
$$[E = VQ]$$

The amount of charge in a circuit depends on the size of the current and how long it has been switched on for. Therefore, charge can be calculated using the following equation:

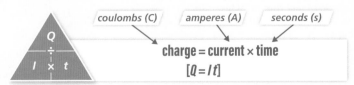

$\dfrac{Q}{I \times t}$

coulombs (C)   amperes (A)   seconds (s)

charge = current × time
$$[Q = It]$$

A 12 V battery supplies a 3.2 A current through a motor for 14 minutes. How much energy is transferred from the battery to the motor?

1 First calculate the charge.

$$Q = It$$
$$= 3.2 \times (14 \times 60)$$
$$= 2,688 \, C$$

2 Now calculate the energy transferred.

$$E = VQ$$
$$= 2,688 \times 12$$
$$= 32,300 \, J \ (3 \text{ s.f.})$$

Power

The power transferred in any electrical circuit depends on the potential difference across it and the current through it.

P ÷ V × I

watts (W)   volts (V)   amps (A)

power = potential difference × current
$$[P = VI]$$

How big is the current in a 2 kW electric kettle connected to the UK (230 V) mains supply?

$$\text{current} = \frac{\text{power}}{\text{potential difference}}$$
$$= \frac{2,000}{230}$$
$$= 8.7 \, A \ (2 \text{ s.f.})$$

Because potential difference = current × resistance, the equation can also be represented as follows:

power = current² × resistance
$$[P = I^2R]$$

When connected to the UK (230 V) mains supply, the resistance of a 100 W filament lamp is measured as 529 Ω. Calculate the current in the lamp filament.

1 First, rearrange the equation to make current the subject.

$$I^2 = \frac{P}{R}$$

2 Now calculate the current in the lamp filament.

$$I^2 = \frac{100}{529}$$
$$I^2 = 0.189$$
$$I = \sqrt{0.189}$$
$$= 0.435 \, A \ (3 \text{ s.f.})$$

Power Ratings for Electrical Appliances

Domestic electrical appliances often have a power rating label that displays information such as the power of the appliance (how much electrical energy it transfers in a second) and the potential difference of the supply. From this, it is possible to calculate the current.

An iron with a power rating of 1200 W is connected to the 230 V mains supply. Calculate the current the iron draws from the mains supply.

$$I = \frac{P}{V}$$
$$I = \frac{1,200}{230}$$
$$= 5.2 \, A \ (2 \text{ s.f.})$$

daydream
EDUCATION

States of Matter

The three states of matter are solid, liquid and gas. In chemical equations, the three states of matter are shown as (s), (l) and (g), with (aq) for aqueous solutions.

States of Matter

Particle theory is a basic model that helps to explain the properties and behaviour of materials in each of the three states. It enables us to visualise what is happening on a very small scale.

Solid

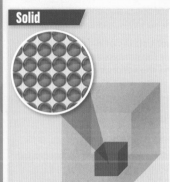

Particle Arrangement & Behaviour
- Strong forces of attraction between particles
- Usually in a regular arrangement
- Particles are close together and vibrate about fixed positions

Properties
- Has a definite shape
- Has a definite volume
- Usually has a high density
- Cannot easily be compressed. The atoms are closely packed together, so there is a lot of mass in a small volume.

Liquid

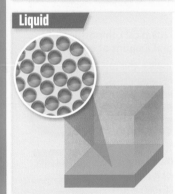

Particle Arrangement & Behaviour
- Weak forces of attraction between particles
- Random arrangement
- Particles move about freely but are close together

Properties
- Takes the shape of its container
- Has a definite volume
- Cannot easily be compressed. The atoms are closely packed together, so there is a lot of mass in a small volume.

Gas

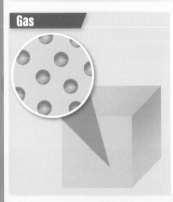

Particle Arrangement & Behaviour
- Very weak forces of attraction between particles
- Random arrangement
- Particles move around freely at high speed and are far apart

Properties
- Takes the shape of its container
- Does not have a definite shape or volume
- Can easily be compressed. The atoms are not closely packed together, so there are few atoms in a given volume.

Limitations

Although particle theory can explain the different states of matter and the differences in density of substances, it has some limitations as a model. For example, particles are not solid spheres, and the forces between the particles are not represented in the model.

State Changes – *Most substances can exist in all three states.*

During a change in state, mass is never lost or gained: it is conserved.

The amount of energy needed to change state – from solid to liquid and from liquid to gas – depends on the strength of the forces between particles in a substance. The stronger the forces, the higher the melting point and boiling point of the substance.

State changes are physical changes that can be reversed. The chemical composition of the particles remains the same, but their arrangement, movement and amount of energy change.

Boiling and evaporation are both changes of state from liquid to gas. Evaporation takes place at any temperature, but boiling occurs only at the boiling point.

Solid   **Liquid**   **Gas**

Melting: when a solid changes into a liquid

Boiling/Evaporation: when a liquid changes into a gas

Heat in
Heat out

Heat in
Heat out

Ice (10 grams)

Freezing: when a liquid changes into a solid

Water (10 grams)

Condensation: when a gas changes into a liquid

Steam (10 grams)

A substance can also change state from a solid to a gas without passing through a liquid phase. This is known as sublimation. For example, dry ice (solid CO_2) sublimates from a solid to a gas at room temperature.

160

Photocopying or scanning this image is a breach of copyright law.

daydream
EDUCATION

Density of Materials

The density of a substance indicates how compact it is. It is measured by mass per unit volume.

The density of a material can be calculated using the following equation:

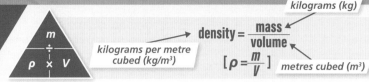

$$\frac{m}{\rho \times V}$$

$$\text{density} = \frac{\text{mass}}{\text{volume}}$$

kilograms (kg)

kilograms per metre cubed (kg/m³)

$$\left[\rho = \frac{m}{V}\right]$$

metres cubed (m³)

Solids and liquids are usually denser than gases. Their atoms are closely packed together, so there is a lot of mass in a small volume. In gases, the atoms or molecules are much further apart, so there is less mass in the same volume.

A balloon contains helium with a mass of 0.00254 kg. The balloon has a volume of 0.0141 m³. Calculate the density of helium.

$$\text{density} = \frac{\text{mass}}{\text{volume}}$$

$$= \frac{0.00254}{0.0141}$$

$$= 0.18 \ (2 \ \text{s.f.})$$

The density of helium is 0.18 kg/m³.

Copper has a density of 8,900 kg/m³. Calculate the volume of 500 g of copper.

$$\text{volume} = \frac{\text{mass}}{\text{density}}$$

$$= \frac{0.5}{8900}$$

$$= 0.000056 \ (2 \ \text{s.f.})$$

The volume of 500 g of copper is 0.000056 m³ or 5.6 × 10⁻⁵ m³.

Practical Activity:
The density of regular and irregular solid objects and liquids can be determined using the following methods.

20 ml

20.00 g

Liquids
1. Place a measuring cylinder on a balance, and set the scale to zero.
2. Pour 20 ml of the liquid into a cylinder, and record the mass.
3. Add another 20 ml of the liquid, and record the new mass and volume.
4. Repeat this process, and then calculate the density of the substance for each set of measurements (1 ml = 1 cm³).
5. Calculate an average density from the results.

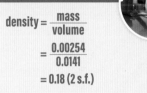

$$V = w \times h \times l$$

Regular Solid Objects
1. Measure the length, width and height of the object.
2. Calculate the volume of the object with the appropriate formula.
3. Measure the mass of the object with a balance.
4. Calculate the density using the mass and volume.

37 ml

20 ml

Irregular Non-Porous Solid Objects
1. Measure the mass of the object with a balance.
2. Pour some water into a measuring cylinder (there needs to be enough water to submerge the object) and record the volume.
3. Place the object into the cylinder, and record the new volume.
4. The difference in volume between the first and second measurement is the volume of the object.
5. Use the mass and volume to calculate the density of the object.

daydream
EDUCATION

Internal Energy & Energy Transfers

Energy is stored inside a system by the particles (atoms and molecules) that make up the system. Internal energy is the total kinetic energy and potential energy of all the particles (atoms and molecules) that make up the system.

Change of State

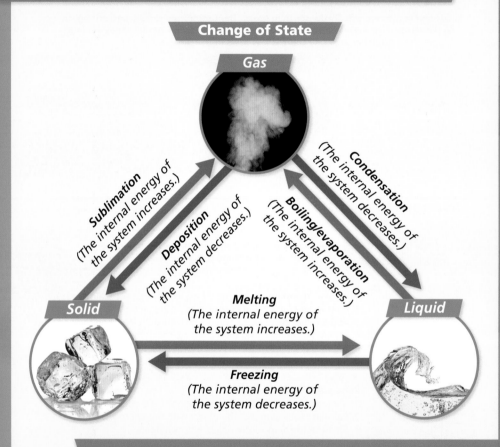

Gas

Sublimation
(The internal energy of the system increases.)

Deposition
(The internal energy of the system decreases.)

Boiling/evaporation
(The internal energy of the system increases.)

Condensation
(The internal energy of the system decreases.)

Solid

Liquid

Melting
(The internal energy of the system increases.)

Freezing
(The internal energy of the system decreases.)

Heating a system increases the energy of its particles, which leads to a change in either temperature or state. A change in state occurs if the particles in the system have enough energy to break their bonds.

Key Point

Temperature (°C) is a measure of how hot something is, whereas heat (J) is a measure of the thermal energy contained within an object.

daydream EDUCATION

Temperature Changes and Specific Heat Capacity

When the temperature of a system is increased by supplying energy to its thermal energy store, the resulting increase in temperature depends upon:

- The mass of the substance
- The type of material (what it is made of)
- The energy put into the system

Therefore, different amounts of energy are needed to increase the temperature of different substances by the same level.

It takes 130 J to increase the temperature of 1 kg of lead by 1°C, whereas it takes 4,200 J to increase the temperature of 1 kg of water by 1°C. Because of water's high specific heat capacity, it is used a lot in temperature regulation.

 Specific Heat Capacity The amount of energy needed to change the temperature of 1 kg of a substance by 1°C

The amount of energy stored in or released from a system as its temperature changes can be calculated by using the equation:

joules (J)   kilograms (kg)   joules per kilogram per degrees Celsius (J/kg °C)

change in thermal energy = mass × specific heat capacity × temperature change

$$\Delta E = mc\Delta\theta$$

degrees Celsius (°C)

Example

How much heat energy is needed to heat 5 kg of water from 15°C to 68°C, given that the specific heat capacity of water is 4,200 J/kg°C?

$$\Delta E = mc\Delta\theta$$

$$= 5 \times 4,200 \times (68 - 15)$$

$$= 1,113,000 \text{ J or } 1,113 \text{ kJ or } 1.11 \text{ MJ}$$

The following investigation is used to measure the specific heat capacity of different metals. The specific heat capacity is determined by linking the decrease of one energy store (or work done) to the increase in temperature of the material.

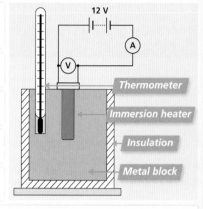

12 V

Thermometer

Immersion heater

Insulation

Metal block

1 Measure the mass of the metal block. The block must have two holes: one for the immersion heater and one for the thermometer.

2 Wrap the metal in an insulating material.

3 Place the thermometer and immersion heater into the holes.

4 Record the temperature of the metal block.

5 Connect the heater to the power supply, set the power pack to 12 V and switch it on.

6 Record the ammeter and voltmeter readings, which should not change. Then calculate the power of the heater in watts:

power = potential difference × current

7 Record the temperature of the metal block every minute for 10 minutes, and then switch off the power supply. Use a table like the one below to record the results.

Time (s)	Temperature (°C)	Power of Heater (W)	Work Done (J)

8 Calculate the energy transferred (work done) by the heater: work done = time × power. Record the results in your table.

9 Plot a graph of the temperature against work done and draw a line of best fit.

10 Calculate the gradient of the straight line:

$$gradient = \frac{change\ in\ temperature}{change\ in\ work\ done}$$

11 Calculate the heat capacity of the block of metal:

$$heat\ capacity = \frac{1}{gradient}$$

12 Calculate the specific heat capacity of the block of metal:

$$specific\ heat\ capacity = \frac{heat\ capacity\ of\ block}{mass\ of\ block}$$

Temperature in °C

Work done in J

Your value for specific heat capacity is likely to be higher than the accepted value. Why do you think this is?

daydream EDUCATION

When a substance changes state, a change in energy is required. This energy is called latent heat.

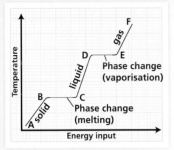

When a substance melts or boils, its internal energy increases. However, the energy is not used to increase its temperature; it is used to overcome the forces of attraction between the particles to enable a change in state.

When a substance condenses or freezes, its internal energy decreases and energy is released. Its temperature does not decrease until the change in state is complete.

 Specific Latent Heat

The amount of energy required to change the state of 1 kg of a substance without a change in the temperature

joules (J)   kilograms (kg)   joules per kilogram (J/kg)

energy for change of state = mass × specific latent heat

$$E = mL$$

Specific Latent Heat of Vaporisation

The amount of energy required to convert 1 kg of a substance from liquid to vapour

Example: The specific latent heat of vaporisation for water is 2,257 kJ/kg. How much energy does it take to evaporate 2 kg of water at 100°C?

$E = mL$
$= 2 \times 2,257,000$
$= 4,514,000$ J or 4,514 kJ

Specific Latent Heat of Fusion

The amount of energy required to convert 1 kg of a substance from solid to liquid

Example: The specific latent heat of fusion for ice is 334 kJ/kg. How much energy does it take to melt 10 g of ice?

$E = mL$
$= 0.01 \times 334,000$
$= 3,340$ J or 3.34 kJ

Particle Motion in Gas

If a gas is kept at a constant volume, changing its temperature will change the pressure. Heating increases the pressure, whereas cooling decreases the pressure.

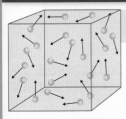

We use the particle model to help us understand, explain and predict the properties of gases.

- The atoms or molecules (particles) in a gas are in constant random motion.

- These particles collide with each other and with the walls of their container without losing any kinetic energy.

- The temperature of the gas is related to the mean (average) kinetic energy of the particles.

When the temperature of the gas increases, so too does the mean kinetic energy of the particles. They move faster, colliding with the walls of their container more frequently and with a greater force. Therefore, the pressure increases.

The Atom

All substances are made of atoms. An atom is the smallest part of an element that can exist.

Development of Atomic Theory

The model of the atom has changed over time as new experimental evidence has been discovered.

1803   1897   1909   1913

Dalton's Model

Atoms were believed to be tiny spheres that could not be divided.

Thomson's Model

After the discovery of electrons, it was proposed that atoms were balls of positive charge with embedded negative electrons. This model is known as the plum pudding model.

Rutherford's Model

Alpha particle scattering experiments found that the mass of the atom was concentrated at its centre in a positively charged nucleus.

Bohr's Model

Experimental observations showed that electrons move around the nucleus in orbits that are a fixed distance from the nucleus.

In **Rutherford's** experiments, alpha particles were fired at a thin piece of gold foil. Rather than pass through the foil as expected, some particles were deflected, and some bounced back.

This meant that the plum pudding model could not be correct, so Rutherford proposed that there must be a positively charged nucleus at the centre of the atom. This model is known as the nuclear model.

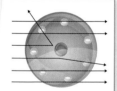

After Bohr's theory of atomic structure was accepted, further experiments by Rutherford showed evidence of smaller positively charged particles (protons) within the nucleus.

This was then developed further, in 1932, with James Chadwick providing evidence to show the existence of neutral particles (neutrons) within the nucleus.

Atoms have no overall electrical charge because they contain an equal number of protons and electrons. Almost all (99.9%) of an atom's mass is in the nucleus.

Atoms turn into positive ions when they lose 1 or more electrons from their outer shell.

Atoms are very small, with a radius of about 0.1 nm (1×10^{-10} m). The radius of a nucleus is less than 1/10,000 of that of the atom (about 1×10^{-14} m).

Particle Name	Relative Charge	Mass
Proton	+1	1
Neutron	0	1
Electron	−1	Very small

daydream EDUCATION

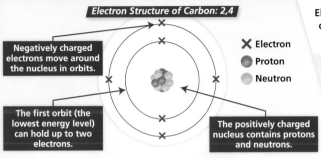

Electron Structure of Carbon: 2,4

Negatively charged electrons move around the nucleus in orbits.

✕ Electron
● Proton
● Neutron

The first orbit (the lowest energy level) can hold up to two electrons.

The positively charged nucleus contains protons and neutrons.

The second and third shells can hold up to eight electrons.

Electrons are arranged in orbits at different distances (and different energy levels) from the nucleus.

If an electron absorbs electromagnetic (em) radiation it may move further from the nucleus to a higher energy level.

If it moves back closer to the nucleus and a lower energy level, it will emit em radiation.

If an atom were blown up to the size of a football stadium, the nucleus would be the size of a small pea on the centre circle. The electrons would be orbiting around the outermost edge, but they would be far too small to be seen.

Atoms and Elements

The number of protons, electrons and neutrons in atoms varies. However, it is the number of protons in the nucleus of an atom that determines what type of atom it is:

Atom	Number of Protons
Helium	2
Oxygen	8
Aluminium	13

All atoms of a particular element have the same number of protons.

An element is a substance that contains only one type of atom and therefore cannot be broken down into simpler components by any non-nuclear chemical reaction.

Atomic Number & Mass Number

Mass Number

The sum of protons and neutrons in an atom

12
C
Carbon
6

Element Symbol

Elements have a one or two-letter chemical symbol. For example, C is the chemical symbol for carbon.

Atomic Number

This is the number of protons (and electrons) in an atom.

Isotopes

Although atoms of an element will always have the same number of protons (and atomic number), they can have a different number of neutrons and, therefore, a different mass number. These are called isotopes.

12
C
Carbon
6

13
C
Carbon
6

14
C
Carbon
6

Radioactive Decay

The nucleus of a radioactive substance is unstable. To become more stable, the nucleus decays and emits radiation.

Isotopes are forms of an element that have the same number of protons but different numbers of neutrons.

The nuclei of some isotopes (radioactive isotopes) are unstable, so they split up or decay, emitting radiation. When a radioactive isotope decays, it can form a different atom with a different number of protons.

Mass number – The total number of protons and neutrons in an atom → 14

Atomic number – The number of protons in an atom → 7

N
Nitrogen

Radiation

When a radioactive substance decays, it emits different types of ionising radiation, including:

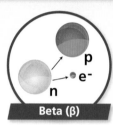
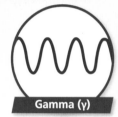

Radiation	Alpha (α)	Beta (β)	Gamma (γ)
Symbol	$^4_2\alpha$ or ^4_2He	$^0_{-1}\beta$ or $^0_{-1}\text{e}$	$^0_0\gamma$
Formation	Two protons and two neutrons are emitted from the nucleus. It is the same as a helium nucleus.	A high-speed electron is ejected from the nucleus as a neutron turns into a proton.	Electromagnetic radiation is emitted from the nucleus.
Penetration	Stopped easily; unable to penetrate skin or paper	Stopped relatively easily; unable to penetrate aluminium (>3 mm thick)	Difficult to stop; unable to penetrate lead (>several centimetres thick)*
Range in Air	A few centimetres	A few metres	A few kilometres
Ionising Power	Very strong due to their size and charge	Moderate	Weak

*Gamma rays have varying amounts of energy because they have different wavelengths and thus different penetrating powers.

daydream
EDUCATION

Activity, measured in becquerel (Bq), is the rate at which unstable nuclei decay. Count-rate is the number of decays recorded each second by a detector, such as a Geiger–Müller tube.

Nuclear Fission

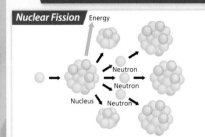

Neutrons are emitted from some very unstable nuclei. The neutrons are a dangerous form of radiation.

Neutron emission is a rare natural occurrence. It can also be made to happen artificially. For example, in a nuclear fission reaction, the parent nucleus releases neutrons as it splits into smaller nuclei.

This example shows the decay of helium-5 into helium-4.

$$^{5}_{2}\text{He} \longrightarrow {}^{4}_{2}\text{He} + {}^{1}_{0}\text{n}$$

Nuclear Equations

The emission of different types of nuclear radiation can cause a change in the mass and/or charge of the nucleus. Nuclear equations are used to demonstrate these changes.

Alpha Decay

Alpha decay causes the mass and charge of a nucleus to decrease. When the nucleus emits two protons and two neutrons, its atomic number reduces by two and its mass number reduces by four.

$$^{222}_{86}\text{radon} \longrightarrow {}^{218}_{84}\text{polonium} + {}^{4}_{2}\text{He}$$

In this example, the radon nucleus emits two protons and two neutrons to form a new polonium nucleus and a helium ion.

Beta Decay

Beta decay causes the charge of a nucleus to increase. When a neutron in the nucleus turns into a proton, its mass does not change. However, the addition of a new proton increases the charge of the nucleus.

$$^{14}_{6}\text{carbon} \longrightarrow {}^{14}_{7}\text{nitrogen} + {}^{0}_{-1}\text{e}$$

In this example, the carbon nucleus decays to form a nitrogen nucleus and a high-energy beta particle.

Gamma Decay

When some nuclei decay by alpha or beta particle emission, they also give out a gamma ray, to leave the nucleus in a more stable state. The gamma ray doesn't change the mass or charge of the nucleus.

$$^{137}_{55}\text{caesium-137} \longrightarrow {}^{137}_{56}\text{barium-137} + {}^{0}_{-1}\text{e} + {}^{0}_{0}\text{Y}$$

In this example, the barium nucleus has excess energy, which is released in the form of a gamma ray.

Remember that the total mass and atomic number on each side of an equation must be equal.

Half-Lives & the Random Nature of Radioactive Decay

Radioactive decay is a completely random process that is not affected by external conditions such as temperature or pressure. Therefore, it is impossible to predict which nucleus in an isotope will decay next or when it will decay.

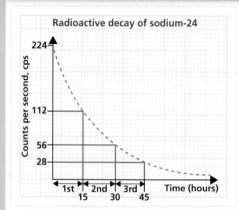

Radioactive decay of sodium-24

You can, however, measure the half-life, or the time it takes for the number of nuclei of the isotope in a sample to halve. You can use this to predict how long it will take for a radioactive source to decay.

The half-life of a radioactive isotope can also be the time it takes for the count rate (activity) from a sample containing the isotope to fall to half its initial level.

The number of unstable nuclei and the activity never reach zero. The time it takes for almost all the unstable nuclei to decay ranges from a millisecond to millions of years.

As shown in the graph, the half-life remains the same throughout the life of the sample.

Example: The initial count rate of a sample of sodium-24 is 224 counts per second (cps) or bequerels (Bq). Its half-life is 15 hours.

1 Calculate the fraction and the percentage of sodium-24 left after 45 hours.

After one half-life (15 h), the count rate decreases to 112 Bq.	$224 \div 2 = 112$
After two half-lives (30 h), the count rate decreases to 56 Bq.	$112 \div 2 = 56$
After three half-lives (45 h), the count rate decreases to 28 Bq.	$56 \div 2 = 28$
The reduction of sodium-24 from 224 Bq to 28 Bq is represented as a fraction.	$\dfrac{28}{224} = \dfrac{1}{8}$
This can be converted into a percentage.	$\dfrac{1}{8} = 0.125$ $0.125 \times 100 = 12.5\%$

2 Determine the ratio of the final count rate to the initial count rate after this time.

Determine the ratio of the final count rate to the initial count rate and reduce.	$28:224 = 1:8$

daydream EDUCATION

Radioactive Contamination

The ionising radiation from a radioactive source can pass into living cells and ionise the atoms in them. The cells can be damaged or killed. As a result, there are significant risks when working with a radioactive source.

Irradiation

The exposure of an object to radiation is known as irradiation. Irradiated objects do not become radioactive, but suitable precautions must be taken to protect against any hazard that the radioactive source may present.

Sources of radiation can be kept in a lead-lined container or at a safe distance away from people. People in contact with radioactive materials can also wear protective clothing and monitor exposure by using a detector badge.

Fruit can be kept 'fresher' for longer by irradiating it with gamma radiation from a radioactive source such as cobalt-60.

The gamma rays destroy any bacteria without altering the fruit in any significant way (although this is subject to debate). Importantly, the process of irradiation does not make the fruit radioactive.

Medical instruments can also be sterilised in this way, especially if standard heat processes might melt the object.

Radioactive Contamination

Radioactive contamination is the unwanted presence of materials containing radioactive atoms on other materials. The radioactive atoms get onto or into an object. For example, you might touch a radioactive source without wearing gloves or breathe in a radioactive gas.

As the nuclei of the contaminating atoms decay, they release potentially dangerous radiation. The level of hazard from the contamination depends on the type of radiation emitted by the decaying nuclei.

Once an object has been contaminated, it is difficult to remove all the radioactive atoms, and the object will continue to be exposed to radiation.

Outside the body, beta- and gamma-emitting sources are the most dangerous because they can penetrate into your body and damage your cells and organs.

α Alpha particles are stopped by your skin so are less dangerous. However, inside the body, alpha radiation is the most dangerous because it has the biggest ionising effect. There is more risk of harm to our bodies from contamination by, rather than irradiation from, alpha-emitting sources.

β Beta-emitting sources are less damaging inside the body. Some radiation passes through the body.

γ Gamma-emitting sources are the least damaging inside the body. Most of the radiation passes through the body. These sources have the lowest ionising power.

It is important for research findings on the effects of radiation on humans to be published and shared among scientists so that the findings can be analysed by peer review.

171

Forces

A force is a push or pull that acts on an object as a result of the object's interaction with another object. Forces are invisible interactions between objects that lead to visible effects such as acceleration.

Scalars and Vectors

A scalar has magnitude (size) only, whereas a vector has magnitude and direction. Forces are vector quantities.

Imagine two cars are travelling at the same speed. If they are travelling in different directions, they have different velocities. This is because velocity is a vector quantity that measures magnitude and direction.

Scalars	Vectors
Speed	Velocity
Distance	Acceleration
Mass	Displacement
Energy	Force

Contact and Non-Contact Forces

Some forces require objects to be in contact (touching) for the forces to interact. For example, friction acts against the movement of two objects rubbing against each other.

Some forces, such as gravity, are non-contact forces that act at a distance.

Contact Forces	Non-Contact Forces
Friction	Gravitational
Air resistance	Electrostatic
Tension	Magnetic

Mass, Gravity and Weight

Mass	Mass is the amount of matter in something. The mass of an object is the same anywhere in the universe.
Gravity	Gravity is the force of attraction between all matter. It varies depending on location. As the distance between two objects increases, the force of gravity between them decreases. All objects have a gravitational force, but gravitational force is directly proportional to mass, so objects with a larger mass also exert a larger gravitational force. An object that is double the mass of another object exerts twice as much gravitational pull.
Weight	Weight is the force acting on an object because of gravity. The weight of an object depends on its mass as well as on the strength of the gravitational field at the point where the object is.

newtons (N) kilograms (kg) newtons per kilogram (N/kg)

$$W = m \times g$$

weight = mass × gravitational field strength
$$[W = m\,g]$$

The weight of an object and the mass of an object are directly proportional: $W \propto m$

The force of gravity close to the Earth is due to its gravitational field. Near the Earth's surface, g is approximately 9.8 N/kg so each kilogram has a gravitational pull of 9.8 N acting on it. The examples below show how the weight of an object varies depending on its location.

Earth
$m = 75$ kg
$g = 9.8$ N/kg
$W = 735$ N

Moon
$m = 75$ kg
$g = 1.6$ N/kg
$W = 120$ N

Mars
$m = 75$ kg
$g = 3.7$ N/kg
$W = 277.5$ N

daydream EDUCATION

The weight of an object can be measured by using a newtonmeter (a calibrated spring balance). The spring is pulled down by the object whose weight is being measured.

The weight of an object is considered to act through a single point, known as its centre of mass.

Free Body Diagrams

Vector quantities may be represented as arrows, such as in free body diagrams.

The length of each arrow represents the magnitude of the force.

The direction of each arrow represents the direction of the force.

Lift

Thrust

Drag

Weight

Resultant Forces

Multiple forces acting on an object may be replaced by a single force that has the same effect as all the original forces. This single force is called the resultant force.

When forces are balanced, the resultant force is zero. A stationary object will remain stationary, and a moving object will continue at the same speed.

If the resultant force is not zero, a stationary object will begin to move in the direction of the resultant force. In contrast, a moving object will speed up, slow down or change direction based on the direction of the resultant force.

$$\overrightarrow{5\,N} - \overleftarrow{5\,N} = 0\,N$$

$$\overrightarrow{10\,N} - \overleftarrow{5\,N} = \overrightarrow{5\,N}$$

A single force can also be split or 'resolved' into two components acting at right angles to each other. Usually one acts horizontally and the other vertically.

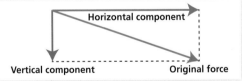

Horizontal component

Vertical component

Original force

Calculating Resultant Forces

If the individual forces are not in the same plane, then the resultant force can be found by using a scale diagram.

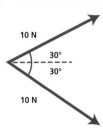

10 N

30°
30°

10 N

Use a ruler and a protractor to make a scale drawing of the forces. Use a sensible scale (e.g. 1 cm per 1 N).

The resultant force is found by adding the two separate forces one after the other (tip to tail) and measuring the total distance (the length of the dashed line).

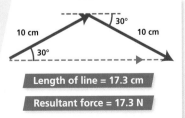

30°

10 cm

10 cm

30°

Length of line = 17.3 cm

Resultant force = 17.3 N

daydream
EDUCATION

Forces & Elasticity

Applying a force to an object causes it to move in the direction of the applied force. However, in order to stretch, compress or bend a stationary object, more than one force is needed.

If an object goes back to its original shape and length after the forces acting upon it have been removed, it has been **elastically deformed**. If an object does not return to its original shape and length after the forces have been removed, it has been **inelastically deformed**.

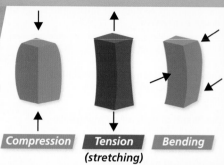

Compression   **Tension** *(stretching)*   **Bending**

The extension of an elastic object, such as a spring, is directly proportional to the force applied provided that the limit of proportionality is not exceeded.

newtons (N)   newtons per metre (N/m)   metres (m)

$$\frac{F}{k \times e}$$

force = spring constant × extension
$$[F = ke]$$

If an object is compressed, the same relationship applies, with e denoting compression.

When forces stretch or compress a spring, work is done and energy is transferred to the elastic potential energy store of the spring. If it is elastically deformed, then all of the energy has been transferred into this store and is equal to the work done on the object.

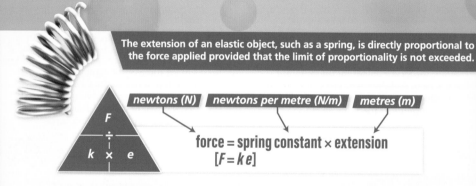

The work done in stretching or compressing a spring (up to the limit of proportionality) can be calculated by using the following equation:

elastic potential energy = 0.5 × spring constant × (extension)²

$$E_e = \frac{1}{2}ke^2$$

As long as the spring has not been inelastically deformed, the work done on the spring and the elastic potential energy stored are equal. If the limit of proportionality is exceeded, the spring becomes permanently deformed and will not return to its original shape and length.

daydream EDUCATION

Practical Activity: Investigate the relationship between force and extension for a spring.

The following practical activity can be used to show the proportional relationship between force and extension (Hooke's law).

1 Set up your apparatus as shown in the diagram. Make sure of the following:

- The ruler is vertical. It is helpful if the zero on the metre ruler is at the same height as the top of the spring.

- The pointer is horizontal, attached securely to the bottom of the spring and rests against the scale of the ruler.

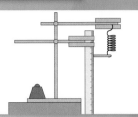

2 Measure the length of the spring before any mass has been added, and record it in a results table like the one shown:

Weight (N)	Length of spring (cm)	Extension of spring (cm)
0		
1		

3 Hook a 100g mass hanger onto the spring. Each time a mass is added to the hanger, you will need to convert it to newtons. A 100g mass exerts a force of approximately 1.0 N.

4 Measure and record the reading on the ruler – that is, the length of the spring when a force of 1.0 N is applied to it.

5 Calculate the extension of the spring.

6 Add further 100g masses to the hanger, and measure and record the length of the spring each time in the table. You also need to calculate and record the extension for each weight.

7 Analyse your results.

a) Use your results to plot a graph with 'Extension (cm)' on the x-axis and 'Weight (N)' on the y-axis. It should give a straight line through the origin.

b) State the relationship between force and extension of the spring.

c) Calculate the spring constant by using the equation:

force = spring constant × extension

d) Calculate the work done in stretching the spring by using the equation:

elastic potential energy = 0.5 × spring constant × (extension)²

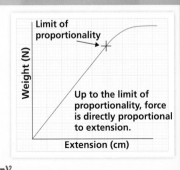

Up to the limit of proportionality, force is directly proportional to extension.

Work Done & Energy Transfer

Work is done on an object when a force causes the object to move through a distance. If the object does not move, no work is done.

The work done by a force on an object can be calculated by using the following equation:

joules (J)   newtons (N)   metres (m)

$W \div F \times s$

work done = force × distance moved (along the line of action of the force)

$$[W = Fs]$$

One joule of work is done when a force of one newton causes a displacement of one metre:

1 joule = 1 newton-metre

Work done against the frictional forces acting on an object causes the object's temperature to rise.

The kinetic energy store of the moving object is transferred to its internal (thermal) energy store.

Example

If a horse pulls a cart with a force of 220 N at a constant speed and covers a distance of 10 m, it is doing work:

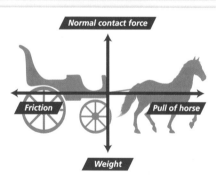

Normal contact force

Friction

Pull of horse

Weight

work done = force × distance moved

$= 220 \times 10$

$= 2{,}200$ N-m or 2,200 J

Some of the horse's chemical energy store is transferred to the cart's kinetic energy store and the internal (thermal) energy store.

daydream
EDUCATION

Forces and Motion

Distance and Displacement

Distance

Distance is how far an object moves. It is a scalar quantity because it does not involve direction.

Displacement

Displacement is a vector quantity that includes the distance an object moves and the direction in which it moves. It is measured in a straight line from the starting point to the finish point.

If you walk 2 km west and then 2 km east, you have travelled a total distance of 4 km. However, your displacement is 0 km.

Example

Elise ran 5 km as shown by the dotted line A to B.

Her displacement is 3 km east.

Distance

A ●..● B

Displacement

Speed and Velocity

Speed is the rate at which someone or something moves. It is a scalar quantity because it does not involve direction. Objects rarely travel at a constant speed. When people walk, run or travel in a car, their speed changes constantly.

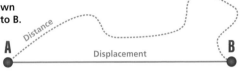

metres per second (m/s) *metres (m)*

$$\text{speed} = \frac{\text{distance}}{\text{time}}$$

$$[v = \frac{s}{t}]$$

seconds (s)

Example

It took Max 5 minutes to drive to the cinema. His mean speed was 15 m/s. How far did Max drive?

$$\text{distance} = \text{speed} \times \text{time}$$
$$= 15 \times (5 \times 60)$$
$$= 4,500 \text{ m}$$

Max drove 4,500 metres, or 4.5 kilometres.

Typical Values of Speed

A person's speed depends upon the individual's age and health, the mode of transport, the terrain being travelled and the length of the journey.

A healthy adult can walk at 1.5 m/s, run at 3 m/s and cycle at 6 m/s.

A car travelling at 30 mph moves at 13 m/s.

The speed of sound in air is 330 m/s, but this can vary.

Distance-Time Graphs

If an object moves along a straight line, the distance travelled can be represented by a distance-time graph.

gradient of graph = speed
The steeper the graph, the faster the speed.

$$speed = \frac{distance}{time}$$

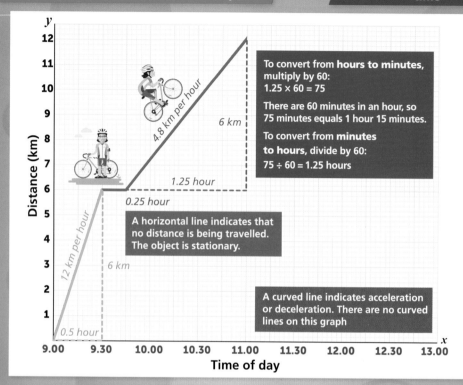

To convert from **hours to minutes**, multiply by 60:
$1.25 \times 60 = 75$

There are 60 minutes in an hour, so 75 minutes equals 1 hour 15 minutes.

To convert from **minutes to hours**, divide by 60:
$75 \div 60 = 1.25$ hours

A horizontal line indicates that no distance is being travelled. The object is stationary.

A curved line indicates acceleration or deceleration. There are no curved lines on this graph

4.8 km per hour

6 km

1.25 hour

0.25 hour

12 km per hour

6 km

0.5 hour

Time of day

Distance (km)

Calculating Speed

To calculate speed at a specific point on a distance-time graph, you can draw a tangent to the curve and then measure the gradient of the tangent.

$$gradient = \frac{change\ in\ y}{change\ in\ x}$$

$$= \frac{200-170}{18-12}$$

$$= \frac{30}{6}$$

$$= 5\ m/s$$

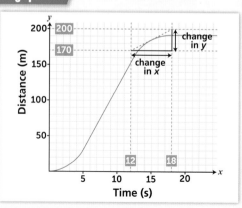

change in y

change in x

Time (s)

Distance (m)

Acceleration

Acceleration is the rate of change of velocity with time. If an object is slowing down, this is called deceleration. If an object is moving in a circular path at a constant speed, then it is still accelerating because of the change in direction.

metres per second squared (m/s²)   metres per second (m/s)

$$\text{acceleration} = \frac{\text{change in velocity}}{\text{time}}$$

seconds (s)

$$a = \frac{\Delta v}{t}$$

Example

An F1 car decelerates from 69 m/s to 25 m/s in 1.2 seconds.

Calculate the deceleration of the car.

$$\text{acceleration} = \frac{\text{change in velocity}}{\text{time}}$$

$$= \frac{25-69}{1.2}$$

$$= \frac{-44}{1.2}$$

$$= -36.7 \, \text{m/s}^2 \, (3 \, \text{s.f.})$$

Uniform Acceleration

The following equation applies to uniform acceleration:

m/s   m/s   m/s²   m

$$\text{(final velocity)}^2 - \text{(initial velocity)}^2 = 2 \times \text{acceleration} \times \text{distance}$$

$$[v^2 - u^2 = 2as]$$

Example

An aeroplane accelerates uniformly from 120 m/s to 240 m/s. During this time, it travels 2 km.

Calculate the aeroplane's acceleration during this period.

$$v^2 - u^2 = 2as$$

$$240^2 - 120^2 = 2 \times a \times 2{,}000$$

$$57{,}600 - 14{,}400 = a \times 4{,}000$$

$$a = \frac{57{,}600 - 14{,}400}{4{,}000}$$

$$a = 10.8 \, \text{m/s}^2$$

Velocity-Time Graphs

Velocity-time graphs show how an object's velocity changes over time.

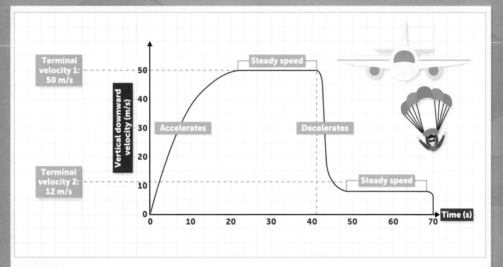

1 A skydiver jumps out of a plane and accelerates due to the force of gravity.

2 As the skydiver speeds up, air resistance increases. This causes the resultant force acting on the skydiver to decrease. The acceleration of the skydiver also decreases.

3 At terminal velocity 1, the force of air resistance (drag) is equal to the force of gravity so the resultant force (and acceleration) is zero.

4 The skydiver deploys her parachute, increasing air resistance and slowing her down.

5 The skydiver's speed continues to slow until the force of air resistance is equal to the force of gravity and terminal velocity 2 is reached.

6 The skydiver lands and decelerates to a halt (rest) in a very short time. The steep graph line shows a large deceleration.

Near the Earth's surface, any object falling freely under gravity has an acceleration of 9.8 m/s². For most objects, this acceleration does not remain constant as the object's speed increases and decreases regularly.

daydream
EDUCATION

When a velocity-time graph is made up of straight lines, the total distance travelled can be calculated by splitting the area into shapes, working out their areas and adding them together.

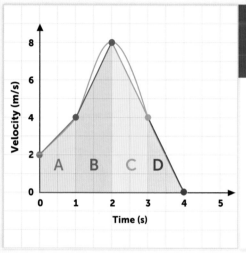

When a graph has curved lines, the total distance travelled is estimated by roughly splitting the area into trapeziums and adding their areas together.

Area A: $\frac{1}{2} \times (2 + 4) \times 1 = 3$

Area B: $\frac{1}{2} \times (4 + 8) \times 1 = 6$

Area C: $\frac{1}{2} \times (8 + 4) \times 1 = 6$

Area D: $\frac{1}{2} \times (4 + 0) \times 1 = 2$

Total: $= 17$

The total distance travelled is 17 m.

The total area under the curved line is likely to be an underestimate because the combined size of the trapeziums is smaller than the actual size of the area under the line.

You can also estimate the total distance travelled by counting the number of squares under the graph and then multiplying this by the distance that each square represents.

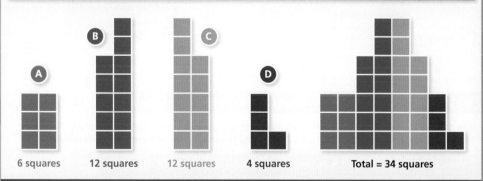

Distance represented by 1 square: distance = **velocity × time** = 1 × 0.5 = 0.5 m

Total distance travelled = **34 × 0.5 = 17 m**

Newton's Laws of Motion

Newton's laws describe the relationship between an object and the forces acting upon it, and its motion in response to those forces.

Newton's First Law

If the resultant force acting on an object is zero, the forces acting upon it are balanced. This means its acceleration will be zero and its velocity (speed and/or direction) constant. Therefore:

A stationary object will remain stationary.

Stationary person

Weight (W)

Free-body diagram

Zero resultant force

F

W

Normal contact force (F)

A moving object will continue to move at a constant speed in the same direction. When a vehicle travels at a steady speed, the resistive forces (friction) balance the driving force (thrust).

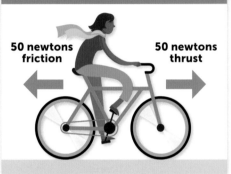

50 newtons friction

50 newtons thrust

Every object has inertia. This is its tendency to continue in a state of rest or uniform motion.

Newton's Second Law

For an object to accelerate (and start moving, stop, speed up, slow down or change direction), the forces acting upon it need to be unbalanced: there needs to be a resultant force.

The acceleration of an object depends on its mass and the resultant force acting on it. This relationship can be represented by the following equation:

newtons (N)

kilograms (kg)

metres per second squared (m/s²)

resultant force = mass × acceleration

$$F = m\,a$$

The acceleration of an object is proportional to the resultant force acting on it: $a \propto F.$

The greater the resultant force acting on an object, the greater the object's acceleration. For example, pedalling a bike faster (i.e. increasing the driving force) increases acceleration.

The acceleration of an object is inversely proportional to the mass of the object: $a \propto \frac{1}{m}.$

An object with a large mass will have a slower rate of acceleration than an object with a small mass if the same force is applied. For example, a greater force is required to push a car than a bike with the same rate of acceleration, because much more force is needed to overcome the car's inertia.

daydream EDUCATION

Calculate the resultant force needed to make a car of mass 800 kg accelerate at 4 m/s².	$F = ma$ $F = 800 \times 4 = 3{,}200$ N
When the car is fully loaded, its mass is 1,200 kg. What resultant force is needed to provide the same acceleration?	$F = ma$ $F = 1{,}200 \times 4 = 4{,}800$ N

The loaded car has a bigger mass than the unloaded car. It therefore needs a bigger force to give it the same acceleration as the unloaded car.

The ratio of force to acceleration is called **inertial mass**: $m = \dfrac{F}{a}$
It is a measure of how difficult it is to change the velocity of an object.

Practical Activity 1

Investigate the effect of varying the force on the acceleration of an object of constant mass.

In this practical activity, you will time how long it takes for a trolley of constant mass to move a distance when different forces are applied.

1 Set up your apparatus as shown.
- Use a ruler to measure 20 cm intervals on the bench, and draw straight lines in chalk at these intervals.
- Attach the pulley to the end of the bench.
- Tie a length of string to the trolley. Pass the string over the pulley, and attach it to the weight stack.

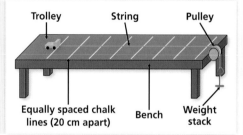

2 Attach 1.0 N to the weight stack, and hold the trolley at the start point.

3 Release the trolley, and as you do, start a stopwatch. Press the stopwatch (lap mode) as the trolley passes each interval on the bench.

4 Create a table like this one and record the results.

Distance Travelled (cm)	1.0 N	0.8 N	0.6 N	0.4 N	0.2 N
			Time (s)		
20					
40					
...					

5 Repeat step 3 with decreasing amounts of weight, and record your results in the table. Place the weights removed from the stack on top of the trolley each time you decrease the weight. This ensures the mass of the system stays the same.

Investigate the effect of varying the mass of an object on the acceleration produced by a constant force.

1 Set up your apparatus as in Practical Activity 1.

2 Select a constant weight for the weight stack, and attach it to the stack.

3 Put a 100 g (0.1 kg) mass on the trolley, and hold it at the start point.

4 Release the trolley, and as you do, start a stopwatch. Press the stopwatch (lap mode) as the trolley passes each interval on the bench.

5 Create a table like the one shown and record the results.

Distance Travelled (cm)	Mass of Trolley (kg)				
	0.1	0.2	...		
20					
40					
...					

6 Repeat step 3 with increasing amounts of mass on the trolley, and record your results in the table.

The results from both activities should confirm the equation linked to Newton's second law: $F = m\,a$.

Newton's Third Law

When two objects interact, the forces they exert on each other are equal and opposite. When an object exerts a force on a second object, the second object exerts the same amount of force on the first object. This is a force pair.

When you push against a wall, the wall pushes back with an equal force. Only the friction between your feet and the floor stops you from moving away from the wall.

When air is released from a balloon, it pushes against the outside air, and the outside air pushes back. As a result, the balloon is propelled forward by the opposing force. This opposing force is known as thrust.

The balloon moves forward as the thrust causes it to accelerate.

It is important to remember that equal forces do not always have the same effect. For example, when a gun is fired, the gun exerts a force on the bullet that pushes it forward, but the bullet also exerts an equal force on the gun that pushes it backwards. However, because the gun's inertial mass is larger than that of the bullet, the gun moves backwards only a small distance.

If the two forces are acting on the same object – for example, a box – it is not an example of Newton's third law. These two forces are not a force pair because they are acting on the same object, the box.

Normal contact force

Weight

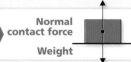

Forces & Braking

When a driver performs an emergency stop, the time and distance it takes for the vehicle to stop depend on the distance the vehicle travels during the driver's reaction time (thinking distance) and the distance it takes for the braking force to stop the vehicle (braking distance).

stopping distance = thinking distance + braking distance

For a given braking force, the greater the speed of the vehicle, the greater the stopping distance.

Braking Distance

Braking distance is affected by multiple factors.

Tyre Condition

Tyre condition affects the traction between a car and the road. Bald tyres do not have much traction with the road, resulting in long stopping distances.

Worn or Faulty Brakes

Worn or faulty brakes can increase a vehicle's stopping distance. This is because they require a greater input force to achieve the same stopping distance as well-maintained brakes.

Adverse Weather

Adverse weather and resulting poor road conditions can reduce the traction between a car and the road. Ice, water and oil can all increase stopping distances.

When a driver applies a force to the brakes, work done by the friction between the brakes and the wheels reduces the wheels' kinetic energy. Energy is transferred from the wheels' kinetic energy store to the brakes' thermal energy store, increasing their temperature.

The greater the speed of a vehicle, the greater the braking force needed to stop the vehicle in a certain distance.

The greater the braking force, the greater the deceleration of the vehicle. Large decelerations may lead to brakes overheating and/or loss of control (skidding).

Speed

There are several factors that can affect the stopping distance of a car.

Speed has a huge influence on stopping distance.

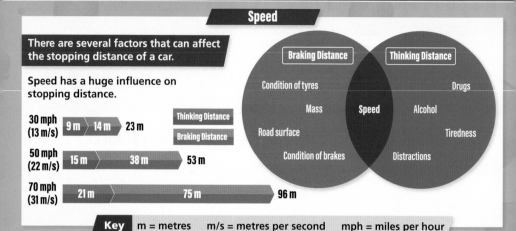

30 mph (13 m/s) 9 m 14 m 23 m

Thinking Distance
Braking Distance

50 mph (22 m/s) 15 m 38 m 53 m

70 mph (31 m/s) 21 m 75 m 96 m

Braking Distance | **Thinking Distance**

Condition of tyres

Mass

Road surface

Condition of brakes

Speed

Drugs

Alcohol

Tiredness

Distractions

Key m = metres   m/s = metres per second   mph = miles per hour

Thinking Distance

Thinking distance is affected by the speed of the vehicle and the driver's reaction time.

Reaction times vary from person to person, from 0.2 s to 0.9 s, and can be affected by drugs, alcohol, tiredness and distractions, such as mobile phones. If the car is travelling at 10 m/s, a reaction time of 0.2 s means the thinking distance is 10 × 0.2 = 2 m. A reaction time of 0.9 s means the thinking distance is 10 × 0.9 = 9 m.

The ruler drop test is used to measure reaction times.

As your partner holds the ruler, stand with your hand in front of you, and position the ruler between your index finger and thumb. The top of your finger should be level with 0 cm on the ruler.

As your partner drops the ruler, catch it as quickly as possible. Measure the point at which you caught the ruler from the top of your thumb.

Repeat three times, and take an average of your results. Typical data for the test is shown below.

Excellent	Good	Average	Fair	Poor
<7.5 cm	<16 cm	<20 cm	<28 cm	>28 cm

daydream EDUCATION

Momentum

Momentum is a property of moving objects. The greater the velocity and/or mass of the object, the greater its momentum.

kilograms metre per second (kg m/s) | kilograms (kg) | metres per second (m/s)

$$\text{momentum} = \text{mass} \times \text{velocity}$$
$$[p = m\,v]$$

Example

A 120 kg rugby player is running at 9 m/s. Calculate his momentum.

$p = m\,v$
$= 120 \times 9$
$= 1{,}080$

The rugby player's momentum is 1,080 kg m/s.

Conservation of Momentum

In a closed system (a system with no external forces), the overall momentum before an event is equal to the overall momentum after the event. This is called the law of conservation of momentum.

Example 1

Trolley A is moving left to right at 2.0 m/s. It collides head on with trolley B, which is stationary. Trolley A stops dead, and trolley B moves to the right. Calculate the final velocity of trolley B.

30 kg | 2.0 m/s | 22 kg | ?
A | B

1 Calculate the overall momentum before and after the collision.

Overall momentum before event	=	Overall momentum after event
p of trolley A before event: $30 \times 2.0 = 60$		p of trolley A after event: 0
p of trolley B before event: 0		p of trolley B after event: $22 \times v = 60$

2 Rearrange the momentum equation for trolley B after the event to calculate its velocity.

$22 \times v = 60$
$v = \frac{60}{22}$
$= 2.73$ kg m/s (3 s.f.)

Example 2

While travelling east, a small car with a mass of 950 kg is involved in a head-on collision with a large car travelling west. The large car has a mass of 2,000 kg. Both cars come to a dead stop in the collision. If the large car was travelling west at a speed of 13 m/s, what was the speed of the small car?

1 Calculate the overall momentum before and after the collision.

Overall momentum before event	=	Overall momentum after event
p of small car before collision: $950 \times v = 950\,v$ kg m/s		p of small car after collision: 0
p of large car before collision: $2{,}000 \times (-13 \text{ m/s}) = -26{,}000$ kg m/s		p of large car after collision: 0

2 The total momentum before an event is equal to the total momentum after the event, so:

$950\,v + (-26{,}000) = 0$
$950\,v = 26{,}000$
$v = \frac{26{,}000}{950}$
$= 27$ m/s (2 s.f.) (moving east)

Waves

Waves carry energy, as well as information, from one place to another. They may be either longitudinal or transverse.

Energy Transfer

When waves travel through a medium, they set up regular patterns of disturbance. The particles of the medium oscillate (move back and forth in a regular rhythm) to transfer energy from one point to another without transferring matter.

For example, when a pebble is dropped into water, the water appears to move outward from the spot where the pebble hit it. However, the water itself does not travel outward, but the waves do.

To further explain this, imagine a bird sat on the water. As the water ripples outward, the bird does not move in the same direction as the waves; it stays in the same place, bobbing up and down on top of the water.

Longitudinal Waves

In longitudinal waves, the oscillations are parallel to the direction of energy transfer.

Example: sound waves travelling through air

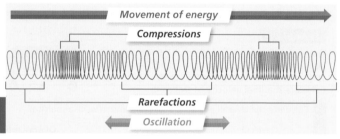

Movement of energy

Compressions

Rarefactions

Oscillation

Transverse Waves

In transverse waves, the oscillations are at right angles (perpendicular) to the direction of energy transfer.

Example: ripples on a water surface

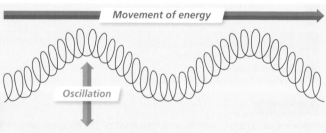

Movement of energy

Oscillation

Wave Properties

Amplitude
The maximum displacement of a point on a wave away from its undisturbed position

Frequency
The number of waves passing a particular point per second; measured in hertz (Hz): 1 Hz = 1 wave per second

Wavelength
The distance from a point on one wave to the equivalent point on an adjacent wave

Period
The time taken for a wave to complete a full cycle

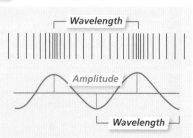

Wavelength

Amplitude

Wavelength

daydream EDUCATION

Period of a Wave

Use the equation below to calculate the period of a wave:

seconds (s)   hertz (Hz)

$$\text{period} = \frac{1}{\text{frequency}}$$

$$T = \frac{1}{f}$$

Example

The frequency of a wave is 50 Hz.

Calculate the period of the wave.

$$T = \frac{1}{f}$$

$$T = \frac{1}{50}$$

$$T = 0.02 \text{ s or } 20 \text{ ms}$$

Wave Speed

Wave speed is the speed at which energy is transferred, or the wave moves, through a medium. Use the equation below to calculate wave speed:

metres per second (m/s)   hertz (Hz)   metres (m)

$$\text{wave speed} = \text{frequency} \times \text{wavelength}$$
$$v = f\lambda$$

Example

A swimmer jumps into a pool, creating a wave. The wave travels at 4.9 m/s and has a wavelength of 40 cm. Calculate the frequency of the water waves.

$$v = f\lambda$$

Rearrange the equation to make f the subject.

$$f = \frac{v}{\lambda}$$

$$f = \frac{4.9}{0.4}$$

$$f = 12 \text{ Hz (2 s.f.)}$$

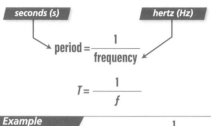

Practical Activity

Investigate the suitability of apparatus to measure the frequency, wavelength and speed of waves in a ripple tank and waves in a solid.

Observing Water Waves in a Ripple Tank

In this activity, you will use a ripple tank to create waves. You can then measure the wavelength and frequency of the water waves to calculate the wave speed.

1 Set up the ripple tank as shown. Place a sheet of white card underneath so the waves can be clearly seen.

2 Pour water into the tank to a depth of 5 mm, and adjust the rod so that it is just touching the water surface.

3 Switch on the electric motor and adjust its speed to produce low-frequency waves that can be counted.

4 Switch on the lamp and adjust its height so that the pattern of the waves can be clearly seen on the white card.

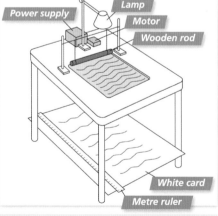

Power supply
Lamp
Motor
Wooden rod
White card
Metre ruler

5 Place a metre ruler at a right angle to the waves shown on the card. Measure across as many waves as you can, and then divide that length by the number of waves to give the wavelength. Record this value in a table similar to the one on the next page.

6 Count the number of waves passing a chosen point in the pattern over a given time (e.g. 10 s). Then divide the number of counted waves by the given time period (e.g. 10 s) to find the frequency of the waves (number of waves per second).

7 Calculate the wave speed with the equation $v = f\lambda$ and record the values in the table.

Frequency (Hz)	Wavelength (m)	Speed (m/s)

Observing Waves on a Stretched String or Elastic Cord

In this activity, you will use a vibration generator to create a stationary wave in a string. You can then measure the wavelength and frequency of the waves to calculate the wave speed.

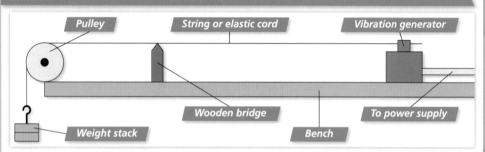

Pulley • String or elastic cord • Vibration generator • Wooden bridge • To power supply • Weight stack • Bench

1 Set up the apparatus as shown, and switch on the vibration generator. The string will start to vibrate.

2 Adjust the tension in the string or move the wooden bridge to adjust the length of the string until you can see a clear stationary wave pattern.

3 Measure across as many loops (half wavelengths) as possible with a metre ruler. Then divide the total length by the number of loops. Multiply your answer by two to calculate the wavelength.

4 The frequency of the waves is equal to the frequency of the power supply.

5 Calculate the speed of the waves, and record this value in a table similar to the one below.

Frequency (Hz)	Wavelength (m)	Speed (m/s)

6 Repeat the steps above for different frequencies.

7 Review and compare the results from both practical activities. Consider how the apparatus used in both activities could be changed to improve the accuracy of the results.

daydream EDUCATION

Electromagnetic Waves

Electromagnetic (EM) waves are transverse waves that transfer energy from the wave source to an absorber. They form a continuous spectrum of different wavelengths but are grouped in order of their wavelength and their frequency.

EM waves travel at the same velocity (3×10^8 m/s) through a vacuum (such as space) or air.

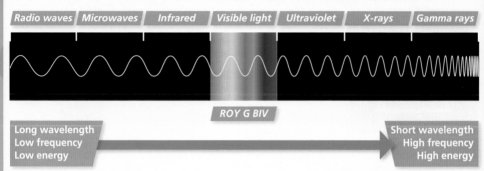

| Radio waves | Microwaves | Infrared | Visible light | Ultraviolet | X-rays | Gamma rays |

ROY G BIV

**Long wavelength
Low frequency
Low energy** → **Short wavelength
High frequency
High energy**

Our eyes can only detect visible light and, therefore, a limited range of EM waves.

Refraction

Depending on their wavelength, EM waves may be absorbed, transmitted, refracted or reflected by different substances.

When waves travel from one medium to another, they change speed and usually direction. This is known as refraction.

A wave will refract towards the normal when it slows down – that is, when it travels from a medium of lower optical density to a medium of higher optical density. Conversely, it will refract away from the normal when it speeds up – that is, when it travels from a medium of higher optical density to a medium of lower optical density.

The acronym FAST can be used to remember this behaviour:
Faster is Away. Slower is Towards.

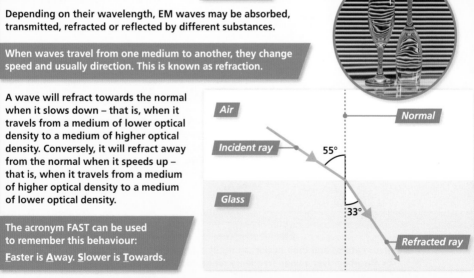

Air
Normal
Incident ray
55°
Glass
33°
Refracted ray

The degree of refraction depends on the comparative optical densities of the two media: the greater the difference in optical density between the two media, the greater the degree of refraction.

daydream EDUCATION

When waves travel from one medium to another, their frequencies remain the same, but their wavelengths change. This is what causes the wave speed to change because:

wave speed = frequency × wavelength
so wave speed ∝ wavelength

This can be represented using wave front diagrams.

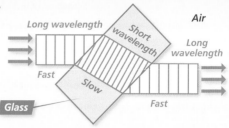

Long wavelength

Short wavelength

Air

Long wavelength

Fast

Slow

Glass

Fast

Waves with different wavelengths refract at different angles. This can be seen when white light passes through a glass prism.

The colours that make up white light (which have different wavelengths) are refracted by different amounts, causing them to disperse (separate).

Radio Waves

Radio waves are not made up of oscillating particles; they are made up of oscillating electric and magnetic fields. Therefore, they can be produced by oscillations in electrical circuits.

How Radio Waves Are Produced With Electricity

Transmitter

Receiver

1	2	3
A high-frequency alternating current (AC) is supplied to the transmitter, causing electrons in the antenna to oscillate.	The oscillating electrons produce oscillating magnetic fields (transverse (EM) radio waves), which have the same frequency as the AC.	When the waves reach the receiver, they are absorbed, causing electrons in the receiver to oscillate. This induces a current of the same frequency as the radio waves.

Changes in Atoms

Changes in atoms and their nuclei can result in EM waves being generated or absorbed over a wide frequency range, including gamma rays.

Gamma rays are produced by the disintegration of unstable (radioactive) nuclei and by the decay of certain particles. The nuclear energy store of the atom decreases when a gamma ray is emitted.

daydream EDUCATION

The Hazardous Effects of EM Waves

Some EM waves can have dangerous effects on human body tissue. These effects depend on the type of radiation and the size of the dose absorbed. The higher the frequency of the radiation, the higher its energy, so the more damage is likely to be caused.

Ultraviolet waves, X-rays and gamma rays all cause mutations to DNA which can lead to cancer. Ultraviolet waves (used in sunbeds) can cause skin to age prematurely and increase the risk of cancer. X-rays and gamma rays are ionising radiation that can also cause cancer.

The size of a radiation dose is a measure of the risk of harm resulting from the body's exposure to the radiation. It is measured in sieverts (Sv). 1000 millisieverts (mSv) = 1 sievert (Sv)

Type	Radio waves	Microwaves	Infrared (IR)	Visible light	Ultraviolet (UV)	X-rays	Gamma rays
Longer wavelength ←							→ **Shorter wavelength**
Lower frequency ←							→ **Higher frequency**
Dangers	Not thought to be hazardous	Heats water in the body; can kill cells	Felt as heat; can cause skin damage & burns	Can damage the eyes	Can cause sun burn, damage to eyes & cancer	Damages eyes and cells; causes cancer	Damages eyes and cells; causes cancer

Uses and Applications of EM Waves

Radio Waves

Radio waves are used to transmit television, radio and communication signals.

Long-wave radio signals can travel long distances because they diffract and follow the curvature of the Earth. Short-wave radio signals do not diffract, but they can travel long distances by reflecting off the part of the atmosphere called the ionosphere.

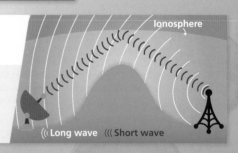

Microwaves

Microwaves are not strongly absorbed by the Earth's atmosphere, so they can be used to transmit signals to and from satellites.

The waves are sent by a transmitter to a receiver on a satellite orbiting the Earth. This satellite then transmits the waves back to Earth, where they are picked up by receivers.

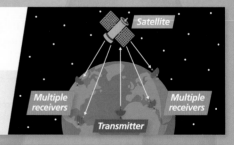

Water molecules in food absorb microwave radiation of certain wavelengths. This causes the water to heat up and cook the food. The water in living cells can also absorb microwave radiation, which can damage or kill living cells.

193

X-Rays & Gamma Rays

X-rays and gamma rays can penetrate our bodies.

X-rays are used in medical imaging. High-frequency X-rays are absorbed by dense body parts, such as bones, but pass through soft body tissues. This enables scanners to create negative images of internal body parts.

Gamma rays and high doses of X-rays can damage and kill living cells. Therefore, they can be used to kill cancer cells (radiotherapy).

Infrared Radiation (IR)

IR is used in electrical heaters, cookers, cameras and detectors.

Visible Light

Visible light enables us to see. It is also used in fibre-optic communications, where data is coded into light pulses, which are sent along glass fibres.

Ultraviolet (UV)

Fluorescent objects absorb UV radiation and emit this energy as visible light.

In fluorescent lights, an electric current is used to excite a gas, causing it to emit UV light. A phosphor coating then absorbs the UV radiation and emits visible light.

Practical Activity: Investigate how the amount of IR absorbed or radiated by a surface depends on the nature of that surface.

A Leslie cube is a hollow metal container that has different surfaces: shiny black, matt black, shiny silver and matt white. An infrared detector can be used to compare the amount of IR emitted from each surface.

1 Put the Leslie cube onto a heat-proof mat.

2 Fill the cube with very hot water, and put the lid on the cube.

3 Use the detector to measure the amount of IR emitted from each surface. Make sure that the detector is the same distance from each surface, and allow enough time between each reading for the detector to settle.

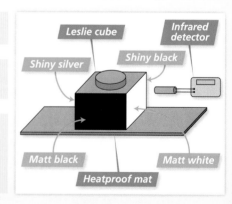

Leslie cube

Infrared detector

Shiny silver

Shiny black

Matt black

Matt white

Heatproof mat

Be careful when performing this experiment as you will be using very hot water.

daydream
EDUCATION

Magnetic Forces

Introduction

A magnet is a material or object that produces a magnetic field.
A magnetic force is a non-contact force exerted by magnets.
It is caused by the motion of electric charges.

All atoms in a substance contain negatively charged electrons that spin, generating an electric current. In most substances, equal numbers of electrons spin in opposite directions, cancelling out their magnetism. However, in magnetic substances such as iron, cobalt and nickel, the electrons spin in the same direction creating a magnetic field.

Magnetic Poles and Magnetic Fields

A magnet has two poles: a north-seeking pole and a south-seeking pole.

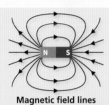

Magnetic field lines

The strength of a magnetic field depends on the distance from the magnet. It is strongest near the poles of the magnet.

Magnetic field lines are used to show a magnet's magnetic field. The closer together the lines are, the stronger the field. The direction of a magnetic field line is from the magnet's north-seeking pole to its south-seeking pole.

The magnetic field of a magnet can be seen by scattering iron filings around the magnet.

Attraction and Repulsion

When two magnets are placed close together, they exert a force on each other.

Two like poles repel each other.

Two unlike poles attract each other.

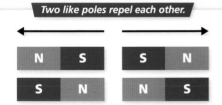

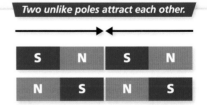

Compasses

The Earth generates its own magnetic field. Therefore, a magnet (in the form of a compass) can be used to find the Earth's magnetic north and south and, consequently, for navigation and orientation.

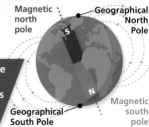

A compass contains a mounted magnetic bar that can spin freely. Because a magnet's poles are attracted to the Earth's magnetic poles, the two points of a compass will align with the Earth's magnetic field. The Earth's magnetic north pole attracts the north seeking ends of magnets, so it is technically the south pole of the Earth's magnetic field.

Magnetic north pole
Geographical North Pole
Geographical South Pole
Magnetic south pole

daydream EDUCATION

A compass can also be used to determine the direction of the magnetic field around a magnet.

The north-seeking pole of a magnet always points towards the south pole of any nearby magnet. Therefore, you can move a compass around a magnet and trace its magnetic field and the direction of its magnetic force.

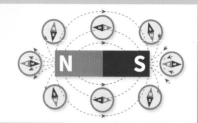

Permanent and Induced Magnets

A permanent magnet produces its own magnetic field. An induced magnet is a material that becomes magnetised when it is placed in a magnetic field.

Induced magnetism always causes a force of attraction. When removed from a magnetic field, an induced magnet loses most or all of its magnetism quickly. This can be demonstrated with a permanent magnet and two iron nails.

When you hold two iron nails together, they do not attract each other because neither is a permanent magnet.

When you place the iron nails next to a permanent magnet, they are attracted to it and become magnets themselves.

Once you remove the nails from the permanent magnet's magnetic field, they lose their magnetism.

1

2

3

No attraction

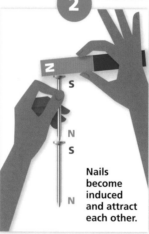

S

N
S

N

Nails become induced and attract each other.

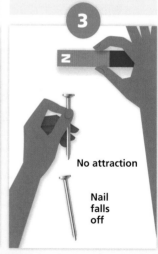

Z

No attraction

Nail falls off

daydream
EDUCATION

Electromagnetism

An electric current in a wire produces a magnetic field around the wire.

The strength of the magnetic field depends on the current through the wire and the distance from the wire. The greater the current, the stronger the magnetic field. The magnetic field is also stronger closer to the wire.

The direction of the magnetic field depends on the direction of the current and can be determined by using the right-hand thumb rule. If you point your right thumb in the direction of the current, your fingers will point in the direction of the magnetic field.

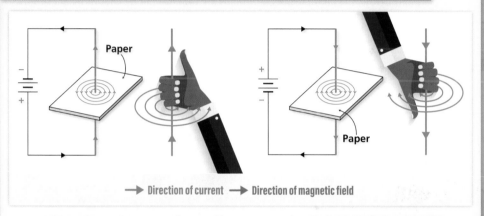

→ Direction of current → Direction of magnetic field

A long wire can be wrapped around a non-magnetic cylinder to make a solenoid. A solenoid increases the strength of a magnetic field created by a current through the wire.

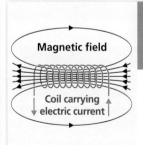

Magnetic field

Coil carrying electric current

Together, the magnetic field lines near each loop of wire result in lots of magnetic field lines pointing in the same direction. This makes the magnetic field inside a solenoid both strong and uniform.

The magnetic field lines have no start point or end point; they are loops. Inside the solenoid, the lines are (almost) parallel and close together, indicating a uniform and strong field. Outside the solenoid, the pattern is very similar to the magnetic field lines created by a bar magnet.

Adding an iron core to a solenoid increases the strength of its magnetic field and creates an electromagnet. However, as soon as the electric current is turned off, its magnetic field disappears.

The Motor Effect

When a conductor (e.g. a wire) carrying a current is placed in a magnetic field, the magnet producing the field and the conductor exert a force on each other. This is called the motor effect.

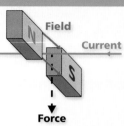

Field
Current
Force

The force is greatest when the wire runs at a right angle to the magnetic field. When the wire runs parallel to the magnetic field, no force is exerted.

In the diagrams below, the invisible magnetic fields are represented by lines of magnetic flux. These lines show the effect, direction and strength of the magnetic field. When magnetic field lines are drawn close together, they show if the magnetic flux density is strong or high; lines drawn further apart show a weak or low magnetic flux density.

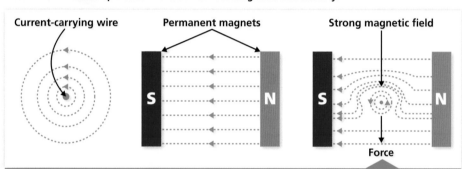

Current-carrying wire
Permanent magnets
Strong magnetic field

Force

In the example above, you can see how the magnetic fields interact when they are at right angles to each other. The force that is produced on the wire is at right angles to the magnetic field and the direction of the current.

Fleming's left-hand rule can be used to find the direction of a force acting on a conductor in a magnetic field.

The size of the force acting on a conductor in a magnetic field depends on the strength of the magnetic field (magnetic flux density), the size of the current through the conductor and the length of the conductor.

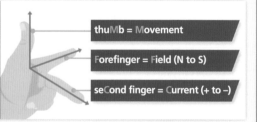

thuMb = Movement

Forefinger = Field (N to S)

seCond finger = Current (+ to −)

For a conductor at right angles to a magnetic field and carrying a current:

newtons (N)   tesla (T)   amperes or amps (A)   metres (m)

$$\text{force} = \text{magnetic flux density} \times \text{current} \times \text{length}$$

$$F = BIL$$

daydream
EDUCATION

Electric Motors

A coil of wire carrying a current in a magnetic field will rotate. This is because the current is flowing in opposite directions in each side of the coil; one side experiences an upward force and the other a downward force. This is the basis of an electric motor.

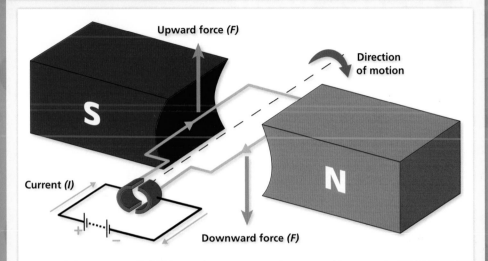

Upward force (F)

Direction of motion

S

N

Current (I)

Downward force (F)

If the direction of the current in the circuit is constant, the coil will not fully rotate. It will get to a vertical position and stop. Therefore, a commutator (a metal ring split into two halves) is used in motors to reverse the direction of the current in the coil every half turn.

In the context of the diagram, this means that the right-hand side always experiences a downward force and the left-hand side an upward force so the coil will fully rotate 360°.

To make the coil spin faster, you could:
- Supply a larger current (by using batteries with a higher potential difference).
- Increase the magnetic flux density (by using a stronger magnet or wrapping the coil onto an iron core).
- Increase the number of turns in the coil.

To make the coil spin in the opposite direction, you could reverse the magnets or the battery.

daydream
EDUCATION

Working Scientifically & Maths Skills

Applications of Science

Scientific developments have led to remarkable discoveries and innovations. However, they have also created issues related to social, economic, environmental and ethical factors. Therefore, the evaluation of scientific applications should consider the advantages and disadvantages related to these issues.

Example: Evaluate the use of zoos to breed animals.

When evaluating something, always remember to consider the arguments for and against.

Social

How do zoos affect people?

- Zoos stimulate interest in animals and provide an opportunity to educate people and to promote animal protection.
- Animals can escape.

Economic

How do zoos affect the economy?

- Zoos create jobs and support local businesses.
- Some zoos donate money to animal charities.
- Zoos can be expensive to run and maintain.

Environmental

How do zoos affect the environment?

- Zoos provide a home for animals that have had their habitats destroyed.
- Removing animals from the wild can further endanger the wild population.

Ethical

Are zoos ethical?

- Zoos save endangered species and can help breed endangered species.
- It is cruel to keep animals in captivity.
- Surplus animals are sometimes killed.

Personal: How do zoos affect you?

Do zoos affect your life in a positive or negative way?

? It is not always possible to answer questions relating to scientific developments, especially ethical questions. This is particularly difficult when there is little or no existing data. Sometimes it can take years of research for new data to come to light.

For example, for years, diesel was promoted as a way of reducing CO_2 emissions. However, in 2012, studies by the European Environment Agency found evidence that nitrogen dioxide (NO2) from diesel fumes were very harmful to human health, causing thousands of premature deaths each year. As a result, there has been a push to phase out diesel cars.

Risk

*A **hazard** is anything that can cause harm.*
Risk is the likelihood of a hazard causing harm.

Measuring Risk

The size of risk posed by something depends on how hazardous (harmful) it is and the likelihood of it happening. Look at the example below:

Lightning is ***very hazardous*** – it can kill.
But the ***likelihood*** of being hit by lightning is ***very low***.
Therefore, the risk of being killed by lightning is low.

Hazards & Risk in Science

There are various hazards in practical science. It is important to identify these hazards and to try to reduce their risk and the likelihood of them occurring and causing harm.

Although scientific or technological developments frequently bring about many benefits, they can also often introduce new risks.

For example, the development of e-cigarettes has helped significantly increase the number of people giving up smoking. However, scientists are still unsure whether the chemicals used in the cigarettes are harmful to the body.

Look at the two examples below. Are the benefits of these technologies worth the risk?

Genetic Engineering

➕ **Benefit:** Genetic engineering can significantly increase food production.

➖ **Risk:** There are serious concerns about the effects of genetically modified foods on human health and biodiversity. Also, gene transfer between plants may lead to an uncontrollable 'escape' of genes into wild plants.

X-Rays

➕ **Benefit:** X-rays are used to check for bone fractures.

➖ **Risk:** Radiation exposure can cause cell mutations that may lead to cancer. However, this risk is thought to be very low.

daydream
EDUCATION

The size of risk posed by a hazard can be measured by looking at the number of times the hazard caused harm in a sample. Look at the example below:

Deaths per 1 billion passenger miles

Motorcycle | 212.57
Car | 7.28

The statistics above show that travelling by motorcycle is riskier than travelling by car.

Perceived Risk vs Measured Risk

The perception of risk is often very different from measured risk.

Familiar vs Unfamiliar

Which has the higher risk?

Running a marathon ← or → **Parachuting out of a plane**

Although most people think parachuting out of a plane is riskier than running a marathon, the risk of dying in both activities is roughly the same: eight in one million. This is because familiar things feel less risky than unfamiliar things.

Visible vs Invisible

Some 3.8 million premature deaths are annually attributed to air pollution. However, because air pollution is invisible, people tend to underestimate its risk. This is the same for many other invisible hazards.

A similar perception applies to hazards that take a long time to take effect, such as an unhealthy diet.

Imposed vs Voluntary

Around 200 years ago, the leading cause of death was communicable diseases caused by poor sanitation and living conditions. People usually did not have a choice about this – the risks were imposed.

Now, the leading cause of death is non-communicable diseases like heart disease and cancer. Often, the risk of these is increased by lifestyle choices, or voluntary risks.

In general, people are more likely to accept the risks that are within their control than the risks over which they have no control.

Apparatus

Scientific apparatus are specialist instruments that are used during experiments. During experiments, it is important to use the correct apparatus, wear the appropriate protective equipment and understand the hazards involved.

Experimental Apparatus

Bunsen Burner
A heating apparatus used in laboratories

Conical Flask
Used for heating and collecting solutions

Filter Paper & Funnel
Used for separating solids from liquids

Test Tubes
Used for heating and testing small quantities of solids and liquids

Clamp Stand
Used to safely hold apparatus in position

Spatula
Used to handle solids and transfer them from containers

Tripod & Gauze
Used to support apparatus above a Bunsen burner

Beaker
Used for stirring, mixing and heating liquids

Evaporating Dish
Used to heat and evaporate liquids

Measuring Apparatus

Measuring Cylinder
Volume – cm³, dm³, ml, l

Stopwatch
Time – s, min

Newtonmeter/ Forcemeter
Force – N

Thermometer
Temperature – °C

daydream EDUCATION

Hazards

A hazard is something that poses a risk and that could potentially cause harm. Hazard symbols are used on containers to indicate the dangers associated with the contents and to inform people about how to use the substance safely.

 Explosive

 Flammable

 Oxidising

 Corrosive

 Toxic

 Health hazard

Safety

Hairnet or Hair Tie

Holds or ties hair back out of the way

Lab Coat

Protects skin and clothes from harmful substances

Safety Glasses

Used at all times to protect the eyes

Risk Assessment

When planning an experiment, complete a risk assessment to identify the hazards, associated risks and the ways in which they can be reduced. It is important to assess the likelihood of something going wrong and the seriousness of the consequences if it does go wrong.

Safety Gloves

Used when handling hot or harmful materials

Peer Review

Peer review is a process that involves the evaluation of scientific, academic or professional work by others working in the same field.

Scientists publish their results in scientific journals. Before a work is published, its validity is checked by experts – this is peer review.

Scientific journals are print and online magazines that contain articles written by scientists about their research.

Science

Searching for Answers

Cell Signalling

Publication can lead to collaborations between scientists to develop ideas or inspire new ones.

It is important that experts review research in journals. Peer review lets readers know that they can be confident that the claims made are valid and believable. However, this does not mean the research findings are correct, just that they are not obviously wrong.

The Peer Review Process

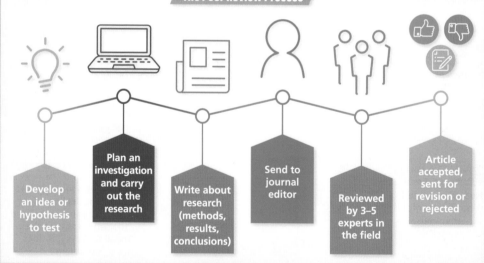

- Develop an idea or hypothesis to test
- Plan an investigation and carry out the research
- Write about research (methods, results, conclusions)
- Send to journal editor
- Reviewed by 3–5 experts in the field
- Article accepted, sent for revision or rejected

Beware!

Scientific reports in the media do not go through peer review so they may be inaccurate or biased. If the report is based on a journal article, get more reliable information by reading the conclusions of the research.

daydream EDUCATION

Planning

A good plan is well designed for its purpose.

Reasons to Plan an Investigation

Make Observations

What structures can be seen in cells?

Produce a Substance

How can a salt be made using neutralisation?

Test a Hypothesis

Is the extension of a spring proportional to the weight added?

Explore Phenomenon

What are wave patterns like in oceans across the world?

What to Think About When Planning

What data or observations need to be collected?
- How many measurements need to be taken to see a pattern?
- What range of measurements is needed?
- How many repeats is enough?

> I need to measure the extension of the spring as the mass on the end changes.

> I will increase the mass by 10 g (0.1 N) until 100 g (1 N) is reached. I will repeat the experiment twice.

What apparatus and techniques should be used?

> I will use a spring held on a clamp stand, a 50-cm ruler and slotted masses.

> I will measure extension by viewing the spring at eye level and taking the reading from the bottom of the spring.

How is the apparatus used to record accurate measurements?

> I will attach the ruler to the clamp stand to make sure it is measuring the length of the spring accurately.

What are the possible hazards? How can the risk of harm be reduced?

> The clamp stand could fall over. Therefore, I will attach the clamp stand to the table with a clamp and make sure it is not placed over my feet.

What are the variables?

> Independent variable = mass
> Dependent variable = length of extension

Variables

Investigations are often performed to identify if there are patterns or relationships between two variables. One variable is changed to see how it affects another variable.

Independent Variable
The independent variable is the one that is changed.

Dependent Variable
The dependent variable is the one that is measured for each change in the independent variable; it's what the investigator thinks will be affected during the experiment.

Control Variables
Control variables are all the other variables in an investigation that should be kept the same to ensure that it is the independent variable that is causing the dependent variable to change.

Presenting Data

Presenting data in an appropriate way makes it easy to spot patterns and draw conclusions from results.

Categorical Data

Includes non-numerical data (e.g. colour) and numerical data with definite values (e.g. number of cells)

Continuous Data

Numerical data that can take any value (e.g. height or time)

A population of plants is found growing in a field, including in a shady area under a tree.

There is lots of data that can be measured to answer the question:

How do light and shade affect plant growth?

Graphing Rules

- Label both axes.

- Give your charts and graphs a title.

- Include a key if you have more than one set of data.

- Usually, the dependent variable goes on the y-axis and the independent variable on the x-axis.

Bar Charts

Bar charts are used to present categorical data. Bar charts help to compare data.

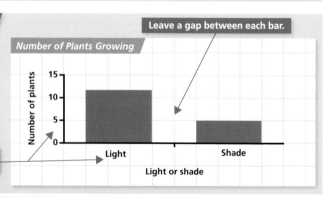

Leave a gap between each bar.

Number of Plants Growing

Number of plants

15

10

5

0

Light

Shade

Light or shade

Use equal intervals on both axes.

daydream EDUCATION

Line Graph

Line graphs are used to display continuous data. They can be used to show trends and change over time.

Change over Time

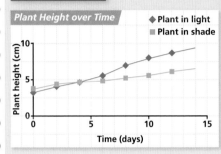

Plant Height over Time
♦ Plant in light
■ Plant in shade

Data is plotted as a series of points that are joined by straight lines.

A Trend

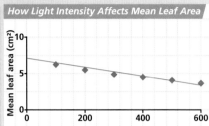

How Light Intensity Affects Mean Leaf Area

A line of best fit can be drawn to show an overall trend and that a proportional relationship exists between the two variables. In this example, as light intensity increases, mean leaf area decreases.

Frequency Tables and Charts

A frequency table is used to record how often a value (or set of values) occurs.

Data from frequency tables is often displayed in frequency charts.

Length of Top Leaf (cm)	Frequency	
	Plants in Shade	Plants in Light
$3.0 \leq l < 3.5$	2	3
$3.5 \leq l < 4.0$	5	7
$4.0 \leq l < 4.5$	4	5
$4.5 \leq l < 5.0$	7	6
$5.0 \leq l < 5.5$	7	4
Total	25	25

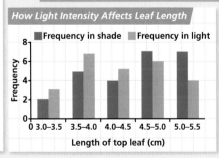

How Light Intensity Affects Leaf Length
■ Frequency in shade ■ Frequency in light

The groups (intervals) must be the same. Make sure to include units of measure in the column headings. A sample of 25 plants from each environment was used. The interval $5.0 \leq l < 5.5$ is equal to or greater than 5.0 and less than 5.5.

Evaluating Data

During data analysis, it is important to be objective and to evaluate data in terms of accuracy, precision, repeatability and reproducibility.

Students performed an experiment to determine how temperature affects reaction rate. They measured the time taken for a certain amount of sulfur to form when sodium thiosulfate solution reacts with acid at different temperatures.

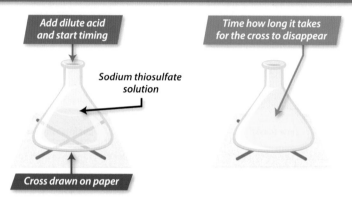

Add dilute acid and start timing

Sodium thiosulfate solution

Time how long it takes for the cross to disappear

Cross drawn on paper

This was measured by determining how long it took for the solution to become completely opaque at different temperatures.

Temperature (°C)	Time for Cross to Disappear (s)		
	1	2	3
10	196	194	196
20	95	88	96
30	53	53	53
40	28	24	26

Precision

Measurements are precise if they are similar and cluster around a single value.

How to Check for Precision: Look how close the repeated values are.

Evaluation: At 30°C, the repeats are all the same, which means these results are very precise. The results at 40°C are not as precise because they have a range of 4 seconds.

Range: the difference between the lowest and highest measurements

daydream
EDUCATION

Accuracy

An accurate measurement is one that is close to the true value. There are few errors and little uncertainty.

How to Check for Accuracy:

Errors: Random errors are shown by anomalous (odd-looking) results, but they can be reduced by taking more measurements and finding the mean value.

Systematic errors are difficult to spot from results, so the equipment should be checked. Any anomalies should be investigated to try and find the cause and, if due to error, should be discarded.

Random error: results varying in unpredictable ways

Systematic error: measurements that differ from the true value by a consistent amount every time; usually caused by a problem with the measuring equipment

Mean

The sum of values divided by the number of values

Example for 40°C: $\dfrac{28 + 24 + 26}{3} = 26$

Percentage Uncertainty

$$\dfrac{\text{range}}{\text{mean}} \times 100$$

Example for 40°C: $\dfrac{4}{26} \times 100 = 15.38$

Uncertainty: The range of measurements around the mean. A low uncertainty is a sign of high accuracy.

Evaluation: The second recorded value at 20°C (88 s) is an anomaly (probably due to a mistake in measurement). The uncertainty is highest for 40°C because these show the most variation around the mean.

Repeatability

Measurements are considered repeatable if they produce similar results when performed by the same investigator under the same conditions.

How to Check for Repeatability:
Look how close the repeats are.
In the experiment above, the measurements show good repeatability because the overall measurements are around the same for each repeated value.

Reproducibility

Measurements are considered reproducible if they produce similar results when performed by a different investigator with different equipment.

How to Check for Reproducibility:
Get someone else to carry out the experiment using different equipment. If their experiment produces similar results to yours, the measurements can be considered reproducible.

Physical Units

International System of Units (SI Units)

Quantity Name	Unit Name	Unit Symbol
Length	metre	m
Mass	kilogram	kg
Time	second	s
Electric current	ampere	A
Thermodynamic temperature	kelvin	K
Amount of substance	mole	mol
Luminous intensity	candela	cd

Other Units

Quantity Name	Unit Name	Unit Symbol
Temperature	degree Celsius	°C
Energy	joule	J
Frequency	hertz	Hz
Force or weight	newton	N
Pressure	pascal	Pa
Power	watt	W
Voltage (potential difference)	volt	V
Resistance	ohm	Ω
Charge	coulomb	C
Capacitance	farad	F

SI Prefixes

These are added to unit names to produce multiples and sub-multiples, or fractions, of the original unit.

Multiples

Factor	Name	Symbol
10^{12}	tera	T
10^{9}	giga	G
10^{6}	mega	M
10^{3}	kilo	k
10^{2}	hecto	h
10^{1}	deca	da

Fractions

Factor	Name	Symbol
10^{-12}	pico	p
10^{-9}	nano	n
10^{-6}	micro	µ
10^{-3}	milli	m
10^{-2}	centi	c
10^{-1}	deci	d

Examples

You need to be able to convert from one unit to another.

10^{3} m (1,000 m) = 1 km 10^{3} g (1,000 g) = 1 kg 10^{-2} m (0.01 m) = 1 cm 10^{-3} g (0.001 g) = 1 mg

Standard Form

Standard form, or standard index form, is used when writing very small or very large numbers.

In standard form, a number is always written in the following format:

A is always a number between 1 and 10: $1 \leq A < 10$

$$A \times 10^{n}$$

n tells you how many places you need to move the decimal point.

Converting Numbers into Standard Form

When writing large numbers in standard form, *n* is always positive.	8,000,000	=	8 × 1,000,000	=	8×10^{6}
	45,000,000	=	4.5 × 10,000,000	=	4.5×10^{7}
	160,000	=	1.6 × 100,000	=	1.6×10^{5}
When writing small numbers in standard form, *n* is always negative.	0.000465	=	4.65 ÷ 10,000	=	4.65×10^{-4}
	0.009	=	9 ÷ 1,000	=	9.0×10^{-3}
	0.0000077	=	7.7 ÷ 1,000,000	=	7.7×10^{-6}

Examples

Example 1

There are around 87,000,000 species on the Earth. Convert this to standard form.

$$87,000,000 = 8.7 \times 10,000,000 = 8.7 \times 10^{7}$$

The decimal point has moved seven places to the left:

8.7000000
7 6 5 4 3 2 1

Example 2

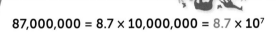

The diameter of the DNA helix is 0.000000002 m. Convert this to standard form.

$$0.000000002 = 2.0 \div 1,000,000,000 = 2 \times 10^{-9}$$

The decimal point has moved nine places to the right:

0000000002.0
1 2 3 4 5 6 7 8 9

daydream
EDUCATION

Rounding to Significant Figures

Significant Figures

If something is 'significant', it is large or important.
Therefore, 'most significant' means 'largest' or 'most important'.

In the number 169.2, the most significant figure is 1 because it has the largest value, 100.	Hundreds	Tens	Ones		Tenths
	1	**6**	**9**	**•**	**2**

The first significant figure in a number is the first digit that is not zero. Any leading zeros are insignificant (placeholders).	0302.14 00.507 0.00621

Rounding to Significant Figures

To round to significant figures, identify the significant figure that is being rounded to and round as normal.

The density of iron is 7.874 g/cm³. To round 7.874 to 2 significant figures:

1	Identify the second significant figure.	7.874
2	Look at the digit to the right of the one that is being rounded. It is more than 5 so round up.	7.874
3	When rounding decimals, there is no need to add zeros after the significant figures.	7.9

7.874 rounded to 2 significant figures is 7.9.

An object has a mass of 0.046748 g. To round 0.046748 to 3 significant figures:

1	Identify the third significant figure.	0.046748
2	Look at the digit to the right of the one that is being rounded. It is less than 5 so leave it alone.	0.046748
3	When rounding decimals, there is no need to add zeros after the significant figures.	0.0467

0.046748 rounded to 3 significant figures is 0.0467.

Taylor ran 400 metres in 52 seconds. Calculate her speed to 2 significant figures.

1	Calculate Taylor's speed: speed $= \dfrac{\text{distance}}{\text{time}} = \dfrac{400}{52} = 7.692307692$ m/s	
2	Identify the second significant figure.	7.692307692
3	Look at the digit to the right of the one that is being rounded. It is more than 5 so round up.	7.692307692
4	When rounding decimals, there is no need to add zeros after the significant figures.	7.7

Taylor's speed to 2 significant figures was 7.7 m/s.

Sampling

It is not always possible to collect information on a whole population. In such instances, a proportion (sample) of the population is used.

Ecologists use a wide range of sampling methods to determine the abundance and distribution of species in an ecosystem.

A larger sample will more accurately reflect the population. A sample that is too small is likely to lead to statistical bias.

Quadrats

A quadrat is a square frame of a specific size (often 0.5 × 0.5 m). It is used to sample an area that is too big to completely survey. The number of one or more species in each quadrat is counted and then scaled up to estimate the number in the whole area.

It would be nearly impossible to count the whole population of daisy plants in a field, but this can be estimated by using quadrats.

Quadrat Example

1	Measure the area of the field.	40 m × 30 m = 1,200 m²
2	Identify how many quadrats are required to provide a sufficient sample area, and calculate the total area.	20 quadrats: 20 × 0.25 m² = 5 m²
3	Place the quadrats in random locations, and count the total number of daisies in each quadrat.	In total, 86 daisies were found in the 20 quadrats.
4	Divide the total area of the field by the area surveyed to identify how much bigger the field is than the survey area.	1,200 ÷ 5 = 240
5	The field is 240 times bigger than the area surveyed. To find an estimate of the total number of daisies in the field, multiply the number of daisies found in all the quadrats by 240.	86 × 240 = 20,640

The accuracy of this estimate can be increased by taking more samples.

Transects

A transect is a line that is used to measure the distribution of organisms, not their numbers. It is usually marked by a rope or tape measure.

Samples are taken at regular intervals along the line, and the species seen at each point are recorded. The line is usually laid along some sort of gradient (e.g. low-tide mark to high-tide mark) to see its effect on distribution.

Averages

An average is a measure of the middle value of a data set. There are three main types of averages: mean, mode and median.

Mean

The mean is the sum of the values divided by the number of values.

$$\text{mean} = \frac{\text{sum of values}}{\text{number of values}}$$

Abbie is measuring her reaction time using the ruler drop test:

Attempt	1	2	3	4	5	6	7	8	9	10
Distance (cm)	19.5	18	12	16	12	10.6	7.5	8	6.4	7

$$\text{Mean} = \frac{19.5 + 18 + 12 + 16 + 12 + 10.6 + 7.5 + 8 + 6.4 + 7}{10} = \frac{117}{10} = 11.7 \text{ cm}$$

Mode

The mode is the value that occurs most often.

The mode for Abbie's results was 12 cm.
It occurred twice, in her third and fifth attempts.

Median

The median is the middle value when the data is arranged in order of size.

Attempt	9	10	7	8	6	3	5	4	2	1
Distance (cm)	6.4	7	7.5	8	10.6	12	12	16	18	19.5

As there is an even number of values, the median is the mean of the middle two values.

$$\text{Median} = \frac{10.6 + 12}{2} = \frac{22.6}{2} = 11.3 \text{ cm}$$

Range

The range is the difference between the lowest value and the highest value in a data set.

Attempt 9
6.4

Range = 13.1

Attempt 1
19.5

To find the range, subtract the lowest value from the highest value.
The range of Abbie's results is 13.1 cm.

daydream EDUCATION

Scatter Graphs

Scatter graphs are used to show how closely two sets of data are related. Correlation describes how the two sets of data are related.

Positive Correlation

When the **plotted points** go upward from left to right, there is positive correlation.

As one quantity increases, the other increases. As one quantity decreases, the other decreases.

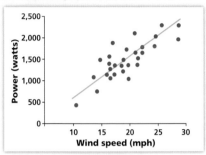

This graph shows that there is positive correlation between wind speed and the amount of electricity generated by a wind turbine. As the speed of a wind turbine increases, so does the amount of electricity generated.

Negative Correlation

When the **plotted points** go downward from left to right, there is negative correlation.

As one quantity increases, the other decreases.

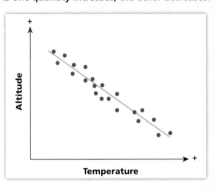

This graph shows that there is negative correlation between altitude and temperature. As altitude increases, temperature decreases.

No Correlation

When there is no linear relationship between two data sets, there is no correlation.

This graph shows that the number of children that a person has is not related to his/her average daily sugar consumption.

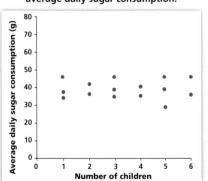

Line of Best Fit

A line of best fit is a line that is drawn through the centre of a group of data points.

When the plotted points are close to the line of best fit, there is **strong correlation**. When they are spread out on either side of the line of best fit, there is **moderate correlation**.

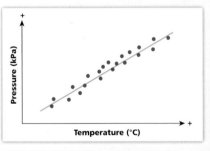

This graph shows a **strong positive correlation**.

Correlation and Causation

A correlation between two variables does not necessarily mean there is a direct cause-and-effect relationship between them.

Example >>> There is a strong positive correlation between germ exposure and disease development. However, these variables are not directly related. Germs alone do not cause disease. The causative factor is a compromised immune system.

Rearranging Formulae

A formula is an equation that shows the relationship between different variables.

Sometimes you can rearrange formulae by using inverse operations to make them easier to work with and solve. In the examples below, the equations have been rearranged to make x the subject:

$x - 4 = 9$ $+4 \quad\quad +4$ $x = 13$	**Addition** and **subtraction** are inverse operations.	$x + 7 = 12$ $-7 \quad\quad -7$ $x = 5$
$mx = t$ $\div m \quad\quad \div m$ $x = \dfrac{t}{m}$	**Multiplication** and **division** are inverse operations.	$\dfrac{x}{r} = 12$ $\times r \quad\quad \times r$ $x = 12r$
$x^2 = w$ $\sqrt{} \quad\quad \sqrt{}$ $x = \pm\sqrt{w}$	Finding the **square root** of a number is the inverse operation of **squaring** that number.	Square $\sqrt{x} = a$ $_2 \quad\quad _2$ $x = a^2$

You can rearrange the formula for speed to make distance or time the subject.

$$\text{speed} = \frac{\text{distance}}{\text{time}}$$

Light travels at an approximate speed of 300,000 km/s. The Earth orbits the Sun at a distance of just under 150 million km.

How long does it take for sunlight to reach the Earth?

1 Rearrange the formula so **time** is the subject.

$$S = \frac{d}{t}$$
$$\times t \quad\quad \times t$$
$$S \times t = d$$
$$\div S \quad\quad \div S$$
$$t = \frac{d}{s}$$

2 Substitute the known values into the formula and solve.

$$t = \frac{150,000,000}{300,000}$$
$$t = 500 \text{ s}$$
$$t = 8 \text{ minutes 20 seconds}$$

You can rearrange the formula for wave speed to make frequency or wavelength the subject.

$$\text{wave speed} = \text{frequency} \times \text{wavelength}$$

The water waves in a ripple tank have a speed of 0.31 m/s and a wavelength of 1.6 cm.

What is the frequency of the water waves?

1 Rearrange the formula so **frequency** is the subject.

$$\text{wave speed} = \text{frequency} \times \text{wavelength}$$
$$\div \text{ wavelength} \quad\quad \div \text{ wavelength}$$
$$\text{frequency} = \frac{\text{wave speed}}{\text{wavelength}}$$

2 Convert the measurement for wavelength from cm to m as wavespeed is measured in m/s. Then, substitute the known values into the formula and solve.

$$1.6 \text{ cm} = 0.016 \text{ m}$$
$$\text{frequency} = \frac{0.31}{0.016}$$
$$\text{frequency} = 19.4 \text{ m/s (3 s.f.)}$$

daydream EDUCATION

Substitution

When substituting in sport, one player is swapped for another. The same principle applies to formulae in science: variables (letters) are swapped with values.

Calculate the potential difference across the battery in the following circuit:

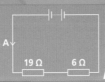

0.4 A

19 Ω   6 Ω

potential difference = current × resistance

1 Calculate total resistance. — 19 + 6 = 25 Ω

2 Substitute the known numbers into the formula. — potential difference = 0.4 × 25

3 Follow the rules of BIDMAS to find the answer. — potential difference = 10 V

Calculate the relative formula mass (M_r) of sulfuric acid.

The relative atomic masses (A_r) needed for this equation are: hydrogen = 1, sulfur = 32, oxygen = 16.

H_2SO_4

1 Write out the formula with the number of atoms. — (2 × H) + (1 × S) + (4 × O)

2 Substitute the relative atomic masses into the formula. — (2 × 1) + (1 × 32) + (4 × 16)

3 Follow the rules of BIDMAS to find the answer. — 2 + 32 + 64 = 98

Matt is measuring his reaction time by using the ruler drop test. The mean distance his ruler dropped is 14.2 cm. Calculate Matt's mean reaction time (in seconds).

$$reaction\ time = \sqrt{\frac{mean\ drop\ distance}{490}}$$

1 Substitute the known numbers into the formula. — $reaction\ time = \sqrt{\dfrac{14.2}{490}}$

2 Follow the rules of BIDMAS to find the answer. — reaction time = 0.17 s (2 s.f.)

Straight Line Graphs

A straight line graph represents a linear relationship, where an increase or decrease in one variable causes a corresponding increase or decrease in the other variable.

Straight Line Equation

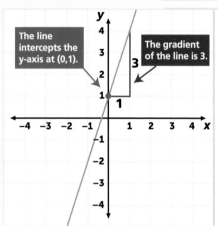

The line intercepts the y-axis at (0,1).

The gradient of the line is 3.

The standard equation of a straight line is:

$$y = mx + c$$

m = gradient of line c = y-intercept

y-intercept = where the line passes through the y-axis

The gradient can be calculated by using the formula:

$$\text{gradient } (m) = \frac{\text{change in } y}{\text{change in } x}$$

The equation of the straight line is: $y = 3x + 1$

$$\text{gradient } (m) = \frac{\text{change in } y}{\text{change in } x} = \frac{3}{1} = 3$$

y-intercept = (0,1)

Finding the Equation of a Straight Line

To find the equation of a straight line, follow the steps outlined below:

1 Find the y-intercept of the graph. This is the value of c. The line intercepts the y-axis at (0,1) so c = +1.

2 Pick two sets of coordinates on the line, and use the following formula to calculate the gradient (m):

$$m = \frac{\text{change in } y}{\text{change in } x}$$

$$= \frac{-1 - -3}{1 - 2}$$

$$= \frac{2}{-1}$$

$$m = -2$$

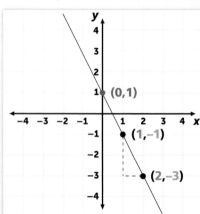

(0,1)

(1,−1)

(2,−3)

The gradient (m) is −2 and the intercept (c) is +1. Therefore, the equation of the line is:

$$y = -2x + 1$$

daydream
EDUCATION

Area, Volume & Surface Area

Area   Area is the total size of a flat surface.

Rectangle/Square

What is the area of the football field?

70 m

100 m

Area of rectangle = length × width

= 100 × 70

Area of field = 7,000 m²

Triangle

What is the area of the sign?

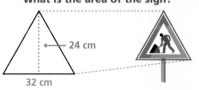

← 24 cm

32 cm

Area of triangle = $\frac{1}{2}$ × base × height

= $\frac{1}{2}$ × 32 × 24

Area of sign = 384 cm²

Volume   Volume is the amount of space inside a 3D shape or object.

Prisms & Cylinders

Volume of prism or cylinder = cross-sectional area × length

Prisms and cylinders are solid objects that maintain a constant cross-sectional area along their length.

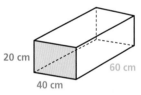 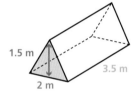 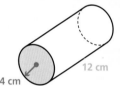

20 cm   60 cm   40 cm

1.5 m   3.5 m   2 m

4 cm   12 cm

V = w × h × l

= 40 × 20 × 60

= 48,000 cm³

V = $\frac{1}{2}$ × b × h × l

= $\frac{1}{2}$ × 2 × 1.5 × 3.5

= 5.25 m³

V = πr^2 × l

= π × 16 × 12

= 603.19 cm³ (2 d.p.)

Surface Area

Surface area is the total area of the outer surface of a 3D object. The surface area of a solid figure is equal to the total area of its net. To calculate the surface area of a shape, work out the area of each face and add them together.

Net

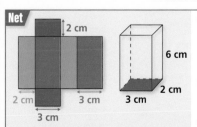

2 cm

6 cm

2 cm

2 cm   3 cm   3 cm

3 cm

Calculate the areas of the different sized faces.

Area = l × w	Area = l × w	Area = l × w
= 3 × 6	= 2 × 6	= 3 × 2
= 18 cm²	= 12 cm²	= 6 cm²

Multiply these areas by the number of corresponding faces.

18 × 2 = 36 cm²	12 × 2 = 24 cm²	6 × 2 = 12 cm²

Add the areas together: 36 + 24 + 12 = 72 cm²

Notes

Index

Index

Index